Spike, or alternate on stem, or axillary

 Amentum

 Corymb

 Umbel

 Flat capitulum

 Cyme, panicle

 Scorpioid cyme

Poisonous parts of the plant

 Flowers and buds

 Seeds

 Leaves

 Roots, bulb, rhizome

 Fruit

 Stem, bark or sap

 Whole plant may be poisonous

Identifying the fungi
Cap

 Concave

 Convex

 Umbonate

 Campanulate, bell-shaped or conical

 Gibbous (ie with humps)

 Warty

 Squamous or fibrillose

 Viscid or glutinous, particularly in wet weather

 Zonal (ie with more or less concentric stripes)

 Hygrophanous (changing colour in wet weather)

 Fleshy

 Thin

 Globular

 On trunks, boles and woody remains

 Humans most at risk
Children

Adults

 Severity of attack
Mild

 Severe

 Possibly fatal

 Treatment
close surveillance and symptomatic treatment

 Prevent further absorption of poison by inducing vomiting if patient is conscious

 Seek medical aid and give artificial respiration if necessary

 Dermatitis
Causes skin irritation and other allergic reactions

Duration of symptoms

 Short term
 Long term
Cumulative effects over a long period

Poisonous Plants

a colour field guide

Lucia Woodward

DAVID & CHARLES
Newton Abbot   London

This publication is simultaneously published by:
Kümmerly + Frey, Bern, in German; Daimon Ediciones, Barcelona, in Spanish; Editions Duculot, Paris and Gembloux, in French; Hippocrene Books, New York; De Nederlandsche Boekhandel, Kapellen, in Dutch; Priuli & Verlucca Editori, Ivrea, in Italian;

joint members of   Club PRIMAVERA

British Library Cataloguing in Publication Data

Woodward, Lucia
  Poisonous plants.
  1. Poisonous plants—Great Britain
  —Identification
  I. Title
  581.6'9'0941   QK100.G7

ISBN 0-7153-8628-X

Typeset by MS Filmsetting Limited, Frome, Somerset
Printed in Italy

CONTENTS

FOREWORD

This book has been written for the general public, for anyone – keen gardener, plant lover, or otherwise – who is interested in knowing a little bit more about the wide variety of wild and cultivated plants which surrounds us. It is intended to call attention to the traps which await the unwary who, responding to the current interest in 'natural' foods, may decide to sample the leaves, fruits, seeds or flowers of many readily available plants.

The author makes no claim to have produced a comprehensive guide, but has covered the area of the more common plants of gardens, fields and hedgerows, woods and wastelands, where the curious and the uninformed may well find a familiar and often much-loved flower or berry and be tempted to add it to the menu – often with disastrous results. Children are most at risk. Every youngster who sees something interesting or attractive tends to put it straight into his or her mouth. How many of us have pulled the succulent stems of long grass and chewed the sap from the ends? How many have looked at the bright autumn berries by the wayside and seen in them free sweets for the taking? Many of our prized garden flowers fall into the category of dangerous plants. The stately delphinium or the hanging tassles of laburnum are good for the eye, but quite a different matter once in the stomach.

The effects which plants can have on man have been known for thousands of years and this knowledge has been exploited for medical, culinary, hallucinogenic and many other purposes. By trial and often fatal error, man has learned what to avoid and what to use, but in this century, with its rapidly increasing use of laboratory-prepared medicines, the knowledge of the traditional herbalist has become restricted to a few specialists; the average layman knows little of the properties of the growing world about him and the old folklore of plants has been largely lost – at least in the Western world.

This book, covering fungi, wild plants, and others commonly cultivated in gardens and homes, is an attempt to guide the unwary adult or child, and to bring help to those who have failed to ask themselves the basic question: 'Yes, I know it – but is it safe?'

HOW TO USE THIS BOOK

The classification of poisonous plants and fungi is extremely problemat-
ical, particularly in a book which is intended to be a quick reference
work. A chemical basis had to be ruled out as far too unfamiliar. A
classification by botanical families was possible; but a mother faced with
a child suffering from the effects of eating some 'black berries' would
hardly know the botanical family those berries are likely to belong to. As
for symptoms, there are so many similar ones; and vomiting or
diarrhoea can be caused by a dozen different plants. I have therefore
tried, as far as possible, to group the plants according to whether you are
likely to find them growing in gardens (your own, your neighbour's or
one you might visit on a Sunday trip), parks and greenhouses; or out in
the wild, in woods, meadows, hedgerows, riverbanks or on moun-
tainsides. The pictograms clearly show the instances where these
habitats overlap: the irises are one example, as they can be found both in
cultivation and in the wild. The fungi have a section to themselves.

The description of individual plants appearing in the captions is
meant only as a useful addition to the information supplied by the
pictograms. The advice given under 'treatment' is by necessity limited:
each case needs different attention according to the particular characteristics of the victim (age, size, sex, general health) and the details
pertaining to the offending substance (quantity, quality, cooked or raw,
etc). As a general rule, the ingested substance should be eliminated from
the system as soon as possible (by vomiting, unless the victim is
unconscious) and medical help or advice should be sought. Always
remember that specific antidotes usually are just not there and
treatment, even in hospitals, is often geared to the symptoms.

By the same token, the seriousness, either in terms of fatality or
duration of the symptoms, cannot be specified exactly for each plant, as
individual cases tend to vary enormously: a plant which can make one
person sick for an hour or so could kill another. There are only a few
clear-cut exceptions.

To sum up, the combination of illustration, caption and pictogram
will give you an idea of what the affected person is suffering from, what
the results are likely to be and what to do about it.

GENERAL INFORMATION

A DEFINITION OF POISONOUS PLANTS

What is a poisonous plant? And what, for that matter, is a poison? Each year the world sees about a million cases of poisoning, thousands of them fatal. The war against poisons has been waged since time immemorial, and yet a satisfactory definition of poison does not seem to have been formulated. Take morphine: in small amounts it is a beneficial drug; in larger doses, and depending on the individual and on circumstances, it is lethal – a poison. Aconitine, on the other hand, is deadly even in quantities of just one milligram. Other substances are harmful without being deadly and, within this broader context, can be regarded as poisons. Even the law does not attempt a definition; the various Poisons Acts merely list the substances which, in its view and for its purposes, can be deemed as such, irrespective of the dosage.

However, a poisonous plant has been defined as 'one which gives rise to a serious departure from normal health, when a small quantity of its fruit, root or vegetation is eaten by a creature which is susceptible to its effects' (Forsyth, 1980). For our own purposes, let us define a poisonous plant as one which contains, in its entirety or in any of its parts, substances which, even in relatively small quantities, can cause varying degrees of disability and even death.

The plants covered in this book are those which most commonly grow in the fields and gardens of Europe and North America. The reader will not find here the upas (*Antiaris toxicaria*) of Java, the pituri plant (*Duboisia hopwoodi*) of Australia, or the soaproot (*Chlorogalum pomeridianum*) of the Californian Indians, however deadly the poison extracted from them may be. But he will be shown the other face of the magnificent delphinium, of the delightful lily of the valley and of the ubiquitous foxglove – not to mention the down-to-earth potato.

Yes indeed, poisonous plants are all around us: as potted houseplants, imported exotics grown in the greenhouse, cultivated hybrids decorating our gardens and even as everyday foodstuffs on the larder shelf. Let us therefore learn to recognise them for what they are and teach our children a long-lost art. After all, prevention is invariably better than cure, and no more so than in the case of our innocent-looking vegetal friends.

B CULTIVATED AND WILD DANGERS

As already said in the section 'How to use this book', I have tried, for the sake of easy reference, to group the poisonous plants according to whether you are likely to find them growing in gardens or in the wild. I did this for several reasons. First of all most people, whether they live in towns or villages or in the heart of the countryside, grow plants one way or another. Even if you have only a windowsill you probably find yourself struggling with a cherished pot-plant or two. In which case, and particularly if children are around, it is not enough to know about these plants' watering requirements. You should also know what can happen if your child chews a piece of what you may have imagined was a harmlessly decorative feature of your living-room (see also p. 12).

On the other hand, if you have a garden of any size, you probably grow lupins, delphiniums, rhododendrons, all sorts of spring bulbs, daphnes and hydrangeas. Once again, it is just as well to know a bit more about these plants than their cultivation requirements. Don't stop growing them, but realise for instance that most bulbs (colchicums, hyacinths, tulips) contain alkaloids which cause, among other symptoms, vomiting and severe purging, sometimes followed by death due to respiratory failure. Children should never be allowed to put them in their mouth to see what they taste like. Deadly alkaloids, one of the commonest causes of plant poisoning in man, can be found in the seeds of the larkspur (*Delphinium ajacis*, No 5), and its cousin the monkshood or aconite (*Aconitum napellus*, No 53) is said to be one of the most dangerous of European plants.

Even if you cannot, or just do not, grow anything at all, you probably take an occasional walk through a park, or visit a botanical garden or drive your family to the country for a day's outing. The range of dangerous plants you are likely to meet on these occasions is even greater. The last two plants mentioned belong to the Ranunculaceae family – a dangerous one for quite apart from what you grow in your garden you can come across its members during any walk through fields or woods any time of the year, and very attractive they are too. Anemones and buttercups, celandines and Pasque flowers are full of charm, and other things besides. The wood anemone (*Anemone nemorosa*, No 58), the Pasque flower (*Pulsatilla vulgaris*, No 38), the common buttercup (*Ranunculus acris*, No 94) and its relative the creeping buttercup (*Ranunculus repens*), the lesser celandine (*Ranunculus ficaria*) and the spearworts (*Ranunculus lingua* and *Ranunculus flammula*) contain protoanemonin in their sap, a substance affected by drying and storage but which can cause dermatitis and serious gastrointestinal troubles if ingested.

Trees can have their dangers too. If not in your own garden, there is a fifty-fifty chance that a laburnum or a horse chestnut (*Aesculus hippocastanum*) is growing somewhere down your street. Children should never be allowed to experiment by tasting the conkers of the latter. Not only do they not taste like sweet chestnuts, but they contain a glycoside (aesculin) which would cause vomiting and diarrhoea. The seeds of the laburnum (*Laburnum anagyroides*, No 24) contain alkaloids which are a common cause of potentially lethal poisoning.

Cultivated and wild plants overlap all along the line. For example the familiar, wild corn poppy (*Papaver rhoeas*, No 89) contains poisonous alkaloids which produce symptoms similar to those of the opium poppy (*Papaver somniferum*, No 34), plus intestinal disturbances. The cultivated species, the Iceland poppy (*Papaver nudicaule*, No 33), is poisonous in all its parts, and so is the horned poppy (*Glaucium flavum*) which grows on shingle beaches. Rhododendron species which can cause delirium are widely cultivated, but they have also naturalised in woods and hillsides throughout North America and in the south and west of Great Britain as well as on the alpine slopes of Europe. Greenhouses have greatly contributed to a general blurring of the division between wild and cultivated. Plants native to the tropics can now be grown in colder latitudes, thus bringing the temptations of gorgeous colours in flowers and fruits literally within the reach of the unaccustomed and the unaware, with sometimes fatal consequences.

This overlap does not apply only to the ornamental plants. Leaves which look like parsley (see No 56, for instance) and roots resembling parsnips may well end up by killing the enthusiast who tries to grow and eat the plant they belong to. If you look for wild herbs or wish to experiment with recipes suggested by the latest book on food from the hedgerows, you should know what to look for and what to guard against. In the world of nature, as much as in any other, appearances can be deadly deceptive.

C FUNGI

Although in Britain the cultivated varieties of the field mushroom are the only ones generally available to the housewife, on the Continent the fungi-eating tradition is much more widespread. As a result, Europeans (either Western or Eastern) have much greater chance both of enjoying a delicious, healthy meal and of being poisoned by another. Some fungi are quite simply inedible because of either their taste or their texture. They are not the fungi we are concerned with here. We are only interested in those that can be eaten by mistake and can do harm when this occurs.

There is absolutely no rule one can follow to distinguish a poisonous from an edible mushroom. All those old-wives' tales about the colour of the flesh when broken, the nature of the ring, the taste, or whether animals eat them or not, are just that – old wives' tales. Neither can one say edible when cooked or dried and poisonous when raw or fresh. This may be true in some cases, but the toxicity of several fungi is not affected by cooking or drying. There is only one way; you must be able to identify beyond all shades of doubt the good from the bad. If you take taste as a guide, for instance, you will find that the amanitas are very palatable; but some of them (*A. virosa, A. phalloides, A. pantherina*, nos 111, 112, 114) are deadly even in very small quantities, whether raw or cooked, fresh or dried.

By the same token, some purplish mushrooms are entirely safe to eat (*Cortinarius violaceus, Laccaria amethystina*): others are good only when cooked and are toxic when raw (*Clitocybe nebularis*, No 121; *Psilocybe semilanceata*, No 140). The discoloration of the flesh when the cap is broken is no more reliable a guide. The deadly *Boletus satanas* (No 118) becomes bluish at first, then reverts to white; the toxic *B. purpureus* (No 117) turns to blue, then red; and the excellent *B. cyanescens* becomes a very deep blue. But *Boletus luridus* (No 116) and *B. erythropus* (No 115) which also turn blue, are poisonous when raw and edible when cooked. As for the deadly amanitas, their flesh is always as white as purity.

Other species are safe when young and harmful when old (*Boletus granulatus* and some of the earthballs). Some exude milk, but even this is not necessarily a pointer to their toxicity. Certain species of *Lactarius* taste and smell too bitter to be tempting, but *Lactarius deliciosus, L. sanguifluus* and *L. volemus* are good in this respect and harmless. The viscosity of the cap cannot be relied upon either, for *Boletus luteus, B. viscidus, Gomphidius viscidus* and others are edible; nor can the fact that some animals do eat certain mushrooms – slugs thrive on the deadly amanitas. There are species of fungi which affect only certain allergic individuals, others which are dangerous only when eaten in large quantities, and still others which can harm when consumed with other substances. *Coprinus atramentarius* (No 122), for example, produces a toxic reaction when accompanied by alcoholic drinks, tea or coffee.

Mushrooms belonging to the *Psalliota xanthoderma* (No 139) group can cause digestive troubles, although not as seriously as fungi such as *Psalliota infida, Clitocybe olearia* (No 137), *Entoloma lividum* (No 125), *Nolanea pascua* (No 136), some *Tricholomas* and boleti. The cholic, diarrhoea and nausea brought on by eating these fungi can be treated, as a first aid, with purgatives, diuretics and copious non-alcoholic fluids. *Amanita muscaria* (No 110) and *A. pantherina* (No 111), together with *Clitocybe dealbata* (No 120), *C. rivulosa, C. cerussata* (No 119), and *C. illudens*, affect the nervous system causing a serious weakening of the heartbeat and breathing difficulties. Purgatives and diuretics can be administered but medical attention is essential. Another toxic fungus, *Russula emetica* (No 141), tastes very sharp and is difficult to eat in quantity; and, should this happen, is usually so quickly expelled from the system (as the name implies, it is a strong emetic) that it has little chance of doing serious damage.

The really deadly fungi include the three amanitas (*A. phalloides, A. verna, A. virosa*, Nos 112, 113, 114). Their poison persists through any treatment and just a few grams can kill an adult. *Gyromitra esculenta* (No 126) can, as its name implies, be eaten safely, but it has been known to cause lethal poisoning: its toxins, however, are destroyed by careful cooking or drying. *Cortinarius orellanus* (No 124) can be a killer, particularly since the symptoms of its poisoning can appear up to two weeks after ingestion. Together with the amanitas and *Lepiota helveola* (No 135), it attacks the liver and kidneys with usually fatal results.

The external appearance of most fungi is very much affected by such variables as weather, temperature and moisture; and age can alter their colour, size, shape and taste. Nevertheless, the plates in this guide will show you what the dangerous species most frequently found in Great Britain and continental Europe usually look like.

D ALLERGENIC PLANTS AND ALLERGIES

Allergenic plants differ from strictly poisonous plants in so far as their effect on the human organism depends entirely on a pre-existing sensitivity. A poison, on the other hand, acts independently of any predisposition. Several books have been written on the subject of allergies, specifically for the family bookshelf, so that what follows is a brief outline of what it is all about.

Basically, an allergy is an oversensitive reaction to a certain stimulant, and as such it affects only certain individuals, usually sporadically. The stimulants, or allergens, can be toxic in themselves or only in the case of these hypersensitive metabolisms. Research is still going on into exactly how it all happens, but what is known is that an allergen (containing protein, like all living cells) stimulates the organism into producing a sort of antibody, called a reagin, the purpose of which is to react against further contacts between the allergen and the organism itself. One of the reactions which take place when further contact occurs is the secretion of histamine in the tissues attacked by the allergen. This in turn leads to an expansion of the blood vessels in the area, increased blood supply (a reddening of the affected area) and increased amounts of blood plasma passing through the capillary walls (a swelling of the area). Such reactions can be localised or, if the histamine is produced in amounts large enough to enter the blood stream, can affect other parts of the body – extreme cases leading to extreme results.

Interestingly, the release of histamine is also linked to emotional and psychological conditions, which thus contribute to render the picture even more complex. Hormones, such as adrenalin, pituitrin and cortisone, also have their effect upon the blood vessels, either by contracting them (the two former ones, released in conditions of stress) or by decreasing their porosity (the latter one, and others). What this seems to indicate is that it is quite possible for a situation to develop whereby if you are allergic to a particular substance or item, such as peppers for instance, your reaction will occur not only if you eat them but also if you just see them!

A tendency to allergy can be hereditary, and sometimes the antibodies (reagins) which cause the allergic reactions can be detected in the blood. As we have seen, allergies develop when the allergenic substance comes into contact with the body, either by being ingested (food allergies) or inhaled (hay fever, asthma) or just touched (dermatitis). None of these should be confused with the body's reactions to poisonous rather than allergenic substances; grass pollen is not poisonous as such, it simply generates an allergic reaction in certain over-sensitive individuals. Food allergies are discussed below; what should be noted here is that the symptoms caused by the ingestion of allergenic substances are often similar to those caused by poisonous substances as they can include vomiting, diarrhoea and abdominal pain.

On the other hand, skin reactions (reddening, itching, blisters and other forms of eruption) are usually caused by allergenics rather than poisons. The most common symptoms, however, are very vague – a general feeling of ill-health, weariness, irritability, depression, and sometimes low temperatures – somewhat unhelpful if you want to discover the cause. And to make matters worse, these symptoms do not necessarily manifest themselves all at the same time. Nevertheless, there may be others to help you in your detective work, such as a sore mouth or tongue, a lot of wind, constipation, and varying degrees of pain in the abdomen. Headache or migraine is, in some cases, related to food allergies. So, if you or a member of your family shows any combination of these symptoms, think back to the ingredients of your meals with the help of the next section.

Inhaled allergenics produce some of the most familiar reactions. Hay fever – if you don't suffer from it yourself you know someone who does – fortunately tends to be seasonal and the sufferer knows when and what to expect and, with luck, what to do about it. It is usually due to plant pollen, any plant's pollen; but particularly wind-borne pollen which is much lighter, better suited to drift through the air and produced in much larger quantities. So be careful when you bring those lovely catkins indoors to decorate your home with the first signs of spring, if anybody in the family is prone to hay fever.

Asthma is a very similar reaction, except that the symptoms are more evenly distributed over the year and point to a more serious irritation of the respiratory tract, including the lungs. The small air passages contract, making breathing difficult, and at the same time the mucous membranes are stimulated into producing secretions in abnormal amounts. Pollen and various dusts have often been found to be the cause of asthma attacks.

Dermatitis is another form of allergic reaction and manifests itself when the contact between the allergen and the human tissue occurs at skin level. You may have touched a particular plant in the course of food preparation, for instance garlic, onions, beans or spices. Or you may have come in contact while tending it, as in the case of certain houseplants (*Philodendron* species or *Pelargonium* species), familiar cultivated plants (calendulas, chrysanthemums, delphiniums, ivies, Christmas roses or even daffodils) or plants in your kitchen garden (globe artichokes, rhubarb, tomatoes). Books specialising in the subject give long lists of plants which have been known to cause such allergic reactions.

It is not always easy to identify the source of an allergy. In the case of asthma and hay fever, complex tests are taken by specialists who would then recommend a course of desensitisation over more or less extended periods according to the particular circumstances, since removal of the offending plant from the everyday environment of the patient may not be possible. Similar tests are also carried out in the case of skin reactions and food allergies, although the cause of these may be more easily identifiable in that you may remember which plant you touched before that eruption developed on your hand, or what particular vegetable was the ingredient common to those meals which made you feel ill. If you do remember, and your suspicions are medically confirmed, then you know what to do about it: keep those plants out of your life! Doctors will then look after your symptoms either by attempting to decrease your body's sensitivity or by prescribing alleviating drugs. The description of such treatments is beyond the scope of this book, which is designed to alert you to the possibilities and help you recognise both the symptoms and their likely causes.

E DANGERS IN THE HOME

There are two ways in which poisonous plants can infiltrate the home – either as ornamentals or disguised as perfectly safe foodstuffs. The latter are of course much more insidious and dangerous, but the former should not be underestimated. Even before the extraordinary increase in popularity recently enjoyed by houseplants, a specimen or two of poinsettia (No 9) were quite commonly grown indoors and constituted an appreciated gift at Christmas. Few households now have never had one, be it red, white or pink, as poinsettias are easy to look after and very decorative in winter. But, they can be lethal. Their sap is caustic enough to produce blistering of the skin; if ingested, any part, be it leaf or bract, produces gastroenteritis symptoms with vomiting, diarrhoea and delirium. Children have been known to die of it. The poinsettia belongs to the Euphorbia family, a few wild members of which can be seen in plates Nos 74, 75, 76; but other cultivated members of this family are potentially dangerous, among them two cacti – the crown-of-thorns cactus (*Euphorbia milli*) and the candelabra cactus (*E. lactea*).

Another pot-plant prized for its decorative qualities is the Jerusalem cherry (*Solanum pseudocapsicum*). Its bright-red or yellow berries, containing alkaloids, are known to have poisoned children, although so far no fatal cases have been reported. *Dieffenbachia seguine* (No 6), one of the dumb canes, is extensively cultivated in homes and greenhouses. If bitten or chewed, the stem of this plant can irritate lips, mouth and tongue; swelling follows, and for several days swallowing and breathing can be difficult.

Some plants are now outlawed in most western countries. It is illegal to grow *Cannabis sativa* (No 67), but the plant has naturalised in many parts, where it is now growing wild, so watch out. It is also illegal to sell the scarlet and jet black seeds of *Abrus precatorius* (precatory bean or rosary pea), which used to be quite common in both Europe and North America strung into colourful necklaces. Their toxins are deadly, one seed containing enough abrin to kill an adult (see p. 22).

While you cannot grow hemp without a special licence, you can still grow your own tobacco (*Nicotiana tabacum*, No 32): only remember that the volatile alkaloid nicotine contained in the leaves is extremely poisonous and can be absorbed through the skin. The same applies to all *Nicotiana* species, particularly the wild tobacco of the United States, and including the common garden varieties.

And while we are on the subject of growing your own, if you buy your tomatoes (*Lycopersicon esculentum*) there is no problem; but if you produce your own, make sure that nobody in the family is tempted to sample the taste of the leaves or stems, as they contain alkaloids of the solanine type. The results of any such sampling would be gastroenteritis and haemolysis of the red cells, with possible damage to the nervous system causing temporary loss of sensation. Fortunately, no fatal cases have so far been reported.

Another common vegetable to watch is the potato (*Solanum tuberosum*, No 47). Here again the green parts contain the toxic glycoalkaloid, solanine, and this can also be found in green or sprouting tubers. Fatalities have been reported in people who had eaten the latter; and if you have any livestock around, particularly pigs, make sure you don't feed them the peelings, vines or sprouts, or you will kill them before you want to.

Tomatoes, potatoes and rhubarb (No 41) are but a few examples of a fairly common characteristic, namely that only certain parts of a familiar plant can be eaten, the others should be carefully avoided as being likely to cause serious poisoning. It is not widely known, for instance, that the pips of apples and pears contain cyanogenetic glycosides which break down into prussic acid. A handful can kill an adult. In fact, a handful did; for there is a well-known recorded case of a man who was so fond of apple pips that, instead of eating them one at a time and at most a few in any day, decided to save them up and treat himself to a cup all in one go. Death by cyanide poisoning followed within a few minutes. The same applies to the kernels of peaches, apricots and plums and to the pips of citrus fruits. They may be bitter to some but not to everybody, as cases of poisoning demonstrate, and children may be tempted to eat them as an 'experiment'.

There are other ways in which dangerous plants can reach the kitchen. The preparation of food may be a causative factor, for in some cases harmful substances are removed only by proper cooking (the mushroom *Lepista nuda*, and some beans, for instance); or they are brought to the fore by eating familiar food in an unusual way. And some plants, perfectly edible by the majority of people, can cause allergies in others.

The normal digestion of proteins can be affected and even inhibited by certain substances often found in the seeds of plants. Soy beans, for instance, should always be well cooked before consumption in order to remove the inhibitors and enhance the beans' excellent nutritional value, for they are rich in proteins. To the soy beans one should add lentils, alfalfa, rice, peanuts, mung beans, runner beans, broad beans, corn and – among the root vegetables – potatoes, beetroot and turnips. Not that one is likely to eat handfuls of such vegetables raw, except perhaps for the broad bean which is delicious raw when young and tender, and even if you did your diet would have to be very unbalanced for you to suffer in any way. Nevertheless, remember the rules, particularly if tempted by such ingredients as bean flour in dishes which are prepared by dry rather than moist cooking.

We have seen how the pips and kernels of some fruits can cause cyanide poisoning if eaten in quantities. Another cyanogenetic substance, linamarin, occurs in certain types of Lima beans, in cassava and flax. Cassava is widely eaten in many parts of the world, and poisoning is avoided by careful washing and cooking. The same applies to that Eastern delicacy, bamboo shoots. Eat as many as you like in your favourite Chinese restaurant, but if they reach your kitchen make sure you prepare and cook them properly.

A particular type of poisoning, known as favism, is caused by the broad bean (*Vicia faba*). When certain individuals inhale the pollen of this plant or eat the raw beans, they develop symptoms ranging from high temperature to delirium. The basic problem is haemolysis (breakdown of the red blood cells); and although recovery usually follows in a few days, death can occur.

The peas, too, have their dangers. The sweet pea (*Lathyrus odoratus*, No 26) is poisonous, so use the plant only for the very rewarding purpose of decorating your home. Its relative, the chick pea, is widely eaten but nevertheless causes problems. In certain countries, for example India, it is staple diet, and here the problems are serious; for the chick pea contains a substance – still not fully identified, but probably amino-acid – which causes the degeneration of the spinal cord and paralysis of the legs (neurolathyrism). It takes several months on a diet based on chick peas before the symptoms such as weakness and gradual loss of the use of the legs appear, but once they have developed their progress cannot be stopped. There is no known cure. Once again, chick peas have a good protein content and their toxic substance is mostly removed by soaking and cooking in plenty of water, and draining after each stage. Their flour, like that of beans, should not be used for dry cooking such as baking.

Goitre, ie the enlargement of the thyroid, is usually due to a deficiency of iodine; but some plants such as cabbages, turnips, radishes and horseradish, contain substances which can affect that gland. However, most dieticians have serious doubts as to whether any of these plants have ever affected humans, since the quantities consumed are usually too small to cause any damage – unless, of course you are allergic to them.

Allergies to foodstuffs are often hereditary and manifest themselves in various ways, ranging from skin reactions to headaches, from respiratory troubles to digestive upsets. The quicker the symptoms appear the more serious the condition is likely to be; if they are slow to manifest themselves, they usually disappear without causing too many problems. Their intensity varies, too – they can be alarming, or so slight as to be barely noticed. A change of diet is the answer, and sometimes it is also the only indication that anything was wrong at all.

If you suspect that food allergy is at the root of your or your child's symptoms, make your point to the family doctor and make it loud and clear. Not everyone in the medical profession is willing to recognise a food allergy in a child's unusual tantrums or in the many mysterious aches and pains which affect people of all ages; often a dangerous situation, which could be easily resolved, is allowed to deteriorate until serious damage is done.

As we have seen in the previous section, a positive identification of the causes of an allergy can only be reached as a result of medical tests. Besides, an allergic reaction to food is a very personal problem, and can be influenced by the way the food is prepared and cooked. However, it has been possible to pinpoint those plants which cause trouble more often than others: the factor to remember is that allergic reactions to any given substance vary widely from person to person and according to age, predisposition, cooking methods, quantity eaten and so on. As a general rule, raw vegetables or fruits are more likely to bring on an attack than cooked ones. Strawberries are a good example, together with bananas, pineapples and other exotics. Among cereals, wheat is a common allergenic, as is rice in its unrefined state, and sometimes rye and barley, corn (maize) and buckwheat.

Familiar vegetables which are sometimes guilty are all beans, some brassicas, turnips and squashes. Peanuts are often in the dock too, together with all sorts of nuts and seeds such as sesame, caraway and poppy, which are often used on bread and other baked products. And if you have a sweet tooth and often suffer from headaches, it may well be all that chocolate you eat.

I have been confronted with guests who say they are allergic to peppers (capsicums), mushrooms and Jerusalem artichokes, although I never dared to put these claims to the test. The thing to do is to remember that anyone can be allergic to just about any food, so keep an eye on the members of your family and ask your guests about any allergies before you cook an expensive meal for them.

A BRIEF LOOK AT THE PAST

The long history of the relationship between man and the plants he eats goes back to the unrecorded annals of tribesmen all over the world whose experience, handed down and built on through the centuries, has brought mankind to the present day when much is known about the effects of eating plants or parts of plants. But the records are yet to be completed, and the toll of poisoning continues, sometimes fatal, often merely unpleasant. Yet it should always be remembered that many plant poisons can have a beneficial effect if used under controlled conditions and that today many common drugs contain plant extracts, themselves lethal yet of tremendous benefit to mankind if used the correct way.

It is estimated that each year there are a million cases of poisoning throughout the world, involving both humans and domestic cattle. There are certainly at least 15,000 deaths, many of them concerning children under five and many caused by the consumption of leaves, seeds and roots. Our ancestors knew a great deal about such poisonings, and had all sorts of antidotes, so let us journey into the past and examine some of the cases which have been recorded.

Hunting and warfare are obvious areas to begin with. Primitive tribes used, and indeed continue to use, poisons distilled from plants for both purposes, tipping their arrows and darts with enough venom to bring down a warrior or an elephant. Aristotle has recorded a story in which Celtic tribes defeated the well-disciplined Romans in 390BC by using poisoned arrows. For their part the Romans frequently won battles by retreating from the field and leaving behind casks of wine spiked with plant poison which merely drugged their 'victorious' enemies; when the potion became effective, and the victors were rendered incapable, the Romans would re-group and massacre their disabled adversaries.

Myth based upon fact features in many a poison story. In the *Odyssey*, Homer relates how the weary voyagers landed on Circe's shores only to be turned into swine by the poison administered by that disagreeable goddess. Odysseus escaped the effect of the poison by drinking a herbal antidote which rendered him immune – a basic attribute of plant poison which has found its way into so many sagas and legends.

Herbalists, botanists and physicians of the ancient world recorded a great many facts which were obviously based upon experience. Nicander of Colophon, the great physician of the third century BC, identified over twenty poisonous plants including hemlock and wolfsbane. Predating Nicander, we read of the ancient Egyptians who discovered a method of extracting lethal cyanide from crushed peach stones and using the concoction as a form of execution, rather as hemlock was used by the Greeks. The execution of Socrates was carried out, in 402BC, by forcing him to drink a potion of hemlock (*Conium maculatum*, No 70) seeds and leaves specially prepared by the public executioner.

Aconite or monkshood (*Aconitum napellus*, No 53) has been recognised as a poison for 2,000 years; a lethal dose kills in fifteen minutes and smaller amounts have been used by witches not to kill but to act as hallucinogens, to give them the sensation of flying. The poppy (*Papaver somniferum*, No 34) has been used as a placid but dangerous poison for inducing a dreamy sleep ever since the earliest recorded times. One of the earliest urban civilisations, the Sumerians, have left clay tablets older than 2000BC which show that the poppy was for them a painkiller and a soporific. The plant was popular with the ancient Egyptians, then with the Greeks who called the seed-juice 'nepenthe', the painkiller and inducer of forgetfulness. Poppy motifs appear on their coins and jewellery; Hesiod, Aristotle and Hippocrates all mention it, as did the Romans Virgil and Pliny, and the Arab Avicenna. So important has the opium poppy been throughout historical times that in the nineteenth century the British East India Company attempted to force the Chinese to accept Indian-grown plants and to establish a lucrative opium trade based in China and exporting to other parts of Asia and the West. China's objection to the virtual poisoning of many of her subjects was overcome by the Opium War of 1839, as a result of which the East India Company was able to grow the opium poppy in China and to export its products to many a lucrative market where the work-weary populace soon succumbed to the dream world of opium peace. It was as late as 1874 that heroin was refined in the West in an attempt to produce a cure for the effects of opium and its by-product morphine. The disastrous industry which flourishes today needs no historical note: it is one example of a plant drug whose use went very wrong indeed. Incidentally, and still on *Papaver somniferum*, story has it that Buddha, while attempting to meditate during his waking hours, found that it was easier to be alert if he cut off his eyelids; these having fallen at his feet produced nodding flowers, the source of sleep for troubled mankind – obviously the opium poppy.

The history of plant poisons is not a neat and tidy story, rather one of periods when the growth of knowledge or the need for temporal power caused certain plants to be used for a specific purpose. During the Italian Renaissance we come across well-documented instances when plants were employed to bring about the fall of many an oligarch or prelate. Plants most popular for the purpose were aconite (*Aconitum napellus*, No 53), hellebore and belladonna. The latter, *Atropa belladonna* (No 64), probably derives its name from Atropos, the Greek Fate who cuts the thread of life. It was used to dilate the pupils of the eyes – supposedly making women look beautiful, hence the name 'bell-adonna', ie beautiful woman – and to cleanse the skin, as well as acting as a basis for poisons to be added to food. So useful was the skill of the poisoner that schools were established to teach the gentle art of adding the lethal to the nutritious. Venice had such a school, which even boasted a code of practice and a scale of fees; and the methods of administering poisons became so sophisticated that the traditional wine-taster could be bypassed while potions were added to meat, water,

17

toothpicks and even to the knife blades used by the victims for cutting their food, or to the wax of the candles which would escort them to their bedchamber – probably for the last time. Long after the Renaissance, in 1882, an Englishman, Dr Lamson, used aconite in order to murder his brother-in-law and inherit his estate. Lamson was unlucky to commit his crime just at the dawn of forensic medicine, and he was caught.

Many of the plants in the long history of more or less accidental poisonings are still common, still beautiful and often still unrecognised as dangerous by the idle and the curious. Oleander, which adds charm to so many houses around the Mediterranean shores and farther east, can be fatal if a single leaf is chewed. There are records of sticks being used to barbecue meat with the result that the oleander poison distilled into the raw meat and killed the would-be camper. Its toxicity has been known since antiquity and there are no records of attempts to use it as a medicinal plant.

Another tree, the toxicity of which has been widely acknowledged throughout the centuries, is the yew (*Taxus baccata*, No 105). Both its leaves and seeds are lethal: once ingested, their alkaloid content is immediately absorbed from the intestine and survival is not common. Yet its wood has always been prized and extensively used; in the Middle Ages it was employed to make bows and since each village was forced by law to supply a certain number of archers, yew had to be grown in quantity. Hence the custom of growing them in churchyards, where their tempting berries would be out of the reach of children and their leaves out of the reach of cattle, sheep and pigs.

We have mentioned cyanide being extracted from peach stones by the ancient Egyptians, but history records many other examples of cyanide poisoning, deliberate and accidental, all based on fruit kernels. Those of the wild black cherry (*Prunus serotina*) and of almonds yield cyanide, as do the already mentioned 'seeds' of peaches, plums and apricots, the stone having to be broken to release the poison. Even that mirror of all great minds, Leonardo da Vinci, is reported to have perfected a method of injecting fruit with potassium cyanide. A brief diet of fruit from his larder is said to have been enough to kill one of the Sforza lords of Milan. Even the pleasant and homely nutmeg, delicious on cakes and custards, has its disadvantages. Historically, it has been used by the Dutch and Portuguese to induce euphoria and it was given to Charles II of England on his deathbed to relieve pain, but in large amounts it is lethal.

One of the curiosities of the vast family of poison plants is the mandrake (*Mandragora officinarum*, No 84), a Mediterranean herb which has given rise to a host of legends and folklore. It was much prized by the herbalists and alchemists of the Middle Ages, which may account for the many stories giving details of why it should not be harvested by the ordinary plant seeker. The root bears some resemblance to the human body and it was said to shriek like a soul in pain when dug up. The plant could only be collected by people of impeccable virtue – possibly herbalists – and certain conditions had to prevail before digging could be carried out. In fact all parts of the plant have been used as an anaesthetic, painkiller, sedative and, of course, poison. In the Bible (Genesis 30: 14–16) Rachel tried to cure her infertility by using it, and early Arab records note that the decomposed root could be used as a poison. The doyenne of poisoners, Lucrezia Borgia, is said to have added it to her lethal repertoire by mixing the powdered root with wine.

The tall and stately hemlock (*Conium maculatum*, No 70), one of the commonest wayside plants of summer and used as a poison since antiquity, was also employed as a narcotic and to combat tetanus and rabies. Mattioli, that ever-curious botanist of the sixteenth century, wrote extensively on the subject of conium poisonings, many of which he had seen and personally attempted to treat. He was the first to recognise the therapeutic and poisonous properties of another plant so often grown in our own gardens, the lily of the valley (*Convallaria majalis*, No 2). He used it to 'tone the brain and heart' and prescribed it against apoplexy, amongst other afflictions. One wonders what happened to any patient who was prescribed an overdose: this was almost certain to be lethal. In 1929, W. Karrer isolated a glycoside called convallatoxin, a very potent heart stimulant used to this day under strict control as a cardiovascular remedy.

Another double-edged remedy, this time a purgative, is the caper spurge (*Euphorbia lathyris*, No 74). It has always been what one might call accident-prone as the fruits strongly resemble the culinary caper (*Capparis spinosa*). The caper spurge fruits are more bitter; and although used from earliest times until the eighteenth century, purging many an invalid from this earth, it was finally replaced by the castor oil plant which is effective and safer – at least under medical supervision (No 43).

The snowdrop (*Galanthus nivalis*, No 11) is interesting. To see its fragile head nodding above the late winter snow is, one hopes, a sign that spring is round the corner; yet its bulb contains toxic alkaloids which may well have made an end of some poor unrecorded peasants in the past as they foraged for sustenance during hard winters. The stinking hellebore (*Helleborus foetidus*, No 15) which breaks cover at about the same time as the snowdrop is not likely to be eaten by cattle or human foragers, but its history as a medicine goes back to facts of antiquity and to classical legend. Hercules used hellebore to cure himself of a bout of madness; earliest records confirm its use against mental illness, and Mattioli cites cases in which he used parts of the plant to control mental attacks. An interesting note comes down to us from Dioscorides, who observed that if the hellebore grows near vines the wine will become purgative when consumed.

Probably even most urban dwellers have a wall on the side of the house where ivy (*Hedera helix*, No 14) has made a home for itself. Whether climbing slowly up wall or tree, this rather charming plant with its evergreen cover and small spurs of berries, is in fact poisonous in all its parts. Ivy has always cropped up as a symbol, oddly enough not as a warning but related rather to some deity. The Egyptians associated it with Osiris; the Greeks depicted Dionysus, god of wine, wearing a wreath of ivy and vines; while below on terra firma Dioscorides used ivy flowers marinated in wine to cure dysentery, applied them externally to ulcers and distilled them to cure earache and toothache. By the Middle Ages ivy was prescribed for a diversity of ailments such as dropsy, headache and jaundice; and the roots were used to cure eye trouble. The ability to apply sound judgement as to how much ivy was beneficial and how much lethal, seems unexplained.

Looking at the gorgeously clad men and women depicted in works of art down the centuries, one may well wonder how they dealt with the parasites that must have been able to make their home amongst so much finery. Certainly our forefathers, rich or poor, needed some protection. Today we have sprays, pyrethrum-based powders, and above all vacuum cleaners. In the Middle Ages the most effective anti-parasite preparation was a good powdering of dried false hellebore (*Veratrum album*, No 107), also effective for the poisoning of arrows, or in milder doses, used against attacks of epilepsy and sciatica.

So many of the plants of our woods and gardens can be dangerous that we can only touch upon a few of historical interest, amongst them a group of ornamental shrubs with a long lethal pedigree – the daphne family, of which *Daphne mezereum* (No 3) is a popular garden plant. The genus has been known for centuries, fruits of *D. gnidium* being used by followers of Hippocrates as a laxative. Galen, the Roman physician who wrote in Greek, was a great believer in the controlled use of daphne, which he prescribed against bilious attacks. In the Middle Ages, while botanists and physicians tried to identify the various species, Mattioli, who seems to have investigated plant properties good and bad all his life, says of the daphne: 'Peasants often use the fruits as a laxative when they feel ill, in the belief they would thus deceive the physicians and chemists; however they do not realise that in so doing they often cause the priests to sing and the bells to toll, as I have often witnessed.'

At last we come to the fungi, to see what history says about them. Fly agaric (*Amanita muscaria*, No 110) is not a killer, but was endowed with quite peculiar properties. For 6,000 years at least this attractive fungus flourished in the vast birch forests of the north, and although such forests retreated further and further north with the end of the last Ice Age, there are still many habitats where the fly agaric can be found. Harvested and eaten it produces hallucinations and visions of a miniature paradise peopled by small creatures – surely the origin of many of the northern fairy tales where the small folk dwell, and the elves and talking wild creatures are found at every turn. The eating of fly agaric created fairyland, and the white-spotted red cap has become one of the illustrative symbols of a world which has enchanted thousands of children who have no idea of the implications.

On a rather different note, it is known that between 90 and 95 per cent of deaths caused by fungi can be attributed to the genus *Amanita*, and particularly *A. phalloides*, *A. verna* and *A. virosa* (Nos 112, 113, 114). Throughout history the 'death cap' must have claimed a huge toll of life, although few specific records remain. Euripides, in the fifth century BC, described the death of four mushroom-eating adults when he visited the town of Icarus. This may well have been caused by one of the amanitas.

Of other poisonous fungi, such as panther cap (*Amanita pantherina*, No 111), common ink cap (*Coprinus atramentarius*, No 122) and yellow stainer (*Agaricus xanthodermus*, No 139), surprising little evidence has been inherited from the botanists and physicians of the past as to how they treated the many cases of poisoning that undoubtedly came to their notice. It is sufficient to say that the gathering of mushrooms and fungi always needs great skill if it is to be safe – a caveat which must have applied ever since primitive tribes roamed the forests.

PLANT POISONS

Why do some plants contain toxic substances? You may well ask! Within the same botanical family, some species may be poisonous, others not; within the same botanical individual, some parts may be poisonous and others not. The answer may lie in evolution, perhaps in a form of self-defence, but this has not yet been established. What is certain is that man only comes into the picture very late, and then purely as an experimenter. Our knowledge of plant poisons has graduated from a trial-and-error approach to a scientific one, and it is this end result that I have tried to present in this book.

Most of the substances which we here call plant poisons fall into two chemical categories – alkaloids and glycosides. There are other substances such as resins and volatile oils which also have toxic effects on the human body, but the former two are the most widespread. Some of these chemicals have medicinal properties when used in the right amounts and in the right preparations, but are lethal when these amounts are exceeded; (for example atropine in deadly nightshade, No 64; and digitoxin in foxglove, No 7).

Such poisons, found in all parts of the plant or concentrated in one or more of them, vary in amount within a given species according to habitat, weather, type of soil, season and age. Their effect – ruled by the age, size, physical condition and sensitivity of the subject affected as well as by the quantity ingested and the treatment the plant has undergone – can be very rapid, becoming manifest within a few minutes, or hours at the most. Other poisons grind away at body cells, slowly and gradually, until the organism succumbs after months or even years.

A THE LARGE GROUPS OF TOXIC SUBSTANCES

Alkaloids These are complex substances named after the alkalis with which they share certain chemical properties. Over 5,000 different types have been found, all containing nitrogen and all acting powerfully on the animal system. They are spread over about 10 per cent of the vegetal kingdom, irrespective of genera or species. (See atropine, colchinine, gelsemine, hyoscyamine, mandragorin and taxine below.)

Glycosides Substances in which a sugar is chemically attached to another molecule:

1 *Cardiac glycosides:* affect the action of the heart. Over 400 have been discovered, mostly in plants related to the lily, the foxglove and the oleander. (See convallamarin, digitalin, helleborein, oleandrin.)

2 *Cyanogenetic glycosides:* So called because they give off cyanide under

the action of certain enzymes. They are present in many plants, in varying amounts according to species or strain. These glycosides are also affected by the weather and by how plants are handled (see amygdalin).

3 *Saponins:* complex glycosides so called because they generate a soapy foam when mixed with water. They can be found in a wide variety of plants and, though not readily absorbed by a healthy digestive system, they attack and destroy the red blood cells (see githagin).

4 *Other glycosides:* these, such as aesculin (*Aesculus hippocastanum*) reduce the ability of the blood to clot.

Goitrogens   Some members of the genus *Brassica* (cabbages etc) have been found to contain substances which can interfere with the body's intake of the iodine necessary for the proper functioning of the thyroid gland. This can result in a shortage of the thyroid hormone and a swelling of the gland itself.

Oxalates   Represented by tiny crystals of calcium oxalates. They cause immediate local irritation when chewed or serious kidney damage if absorbed into the system (see Nos 6, 61, 62, 63).

Phytotoxins   These consist of large protein molecules and are affected by prolonged heating. Usually found in some of the most toxic plants known (eg *Ricinus communis*, No 43), they are not affected by the digestive process – which makes them extremely dangerous.

Resinoids   Complex substances, all widely different chemically but similar in so far as, when extracted, they are semi-solid (at room temperature) and can easily be burnt or melted (see andromedotoxin).

B SOME SPECIFIC POISONS

When looking at individual plants in the plates section, you will come across the names of toxic substances which are characteristic of one plant or another. Although these substances belong to the larger groupings listed above, much as a botanical genus or species belongs to a botanical family, it is worth having a closer look at them and their effects to get to know them better.

Abrin   (*Abrus precatorius*)   A poisonous compound contained in the highly decorative seeds which are (or were) used for bracelets and necklaces; in many countries they are now outlawed. The poison can be absorbed through the skin when perspiration occurs. Should just one seed be chewed and swallowed, death is almost certain. The symptoms may not appear immediately, sometimes not for a few days, then there is loss of appetite, stomach upset, vomiting, diarrhoea, cold perspiration, accelerated pulse, delirium and total collapse. There is no known antidote. Immediate medical help should be sought.

Aconitine   (*Aconitum napellus*, No 53)   Another deadly compound. Just one milligram can kill, taking anything between eight minutes and four hours; and the poison is contained in all parts of the plant. Immediate symptoms are a tingling of the mouth, throat and face, followed by numbness, giddiness, slow heartbeat, loss of muscular power, vomiting, diarrhoea, convulsion and death through paralysis of the breathing muscles or cardiac failure. One should immediately seek professional help.

Amanitine (*Amanita phalloides*, No 112) In its alpha, beta and gamma forms, one of the five powerful poisons contained in this mushroom. It becomes active some six to eight days after the victim has survived the agonising attacks of phalloidin (see p. 25), the first lethal substance he or she has to cope with.

Amanitine is a hundred times as strong as cyanide; it paralyses the kidneys and disintegrates the liver cells, it causes hallucinations and finally death of the brain. As little as a third of a cap of this fungus can be fatal, cooked or raw. Mortality is exceedingly high as, by the time the symptoms first appear, the toxins have already been absorbed into the system. Even if the victim survives, the damage caused to the cells of the various organs can have lifelong effects.

Amygdalin (*Prunus serotina*, see p 182) A cyanogenetic glycoside which, when broken into its components by the stomach enzymes, yields hydrogen cyanide. A few chewed leaves can cause death within the hour.

Similar cyanide compounds are found in the kernels of peaches, plums, apricots, cherries and almonds, and in the pips of apples. Hydrogen cyanide gas inhibits the use of oxygen by the tissue cells and paralyses the centre of the brain which controls the breathing muscles (see also cyanide).

Andromedotoxin (*Rhododendron* spp. Nos 42, 97; *Kalmia* spp. No 23) Like *Veratrum* alkaloids, this resinoid substance produces salivation, vomiting, sweating, hypotension, depression of the striated muscles and of the central nervous system, shallow respiration, irregular pulse and bradycardia followed by convulsions and death from asphyxia. It can only be treated professionally with gastric lavage and the use of various drugs to support respiration, counteract bradycardia, induce emesis and treat hypotension.

Arbutin (*Kalmia* spp. No 23) A glycoside of hydroquinone suggested by some authors as the cause of most of the toxicity symptoms, such as gastroenteritis, vomiting, abdominal pain and breathing difficulties.

Atropine (*Cestrum nocturnum*, *Datura stramonium*, No 72) An alkaloid which affects the muscles and the respiratory and circulatory systems. First symptoms are thirst and vision disturbance. It can be fatal in conjunction with other alkaloids (see stramonine). It is also used for beneficial medical purposes.

Bryonin (*Bryonia dioica*, No 65) A glycoside contained in the roots and berries of this plant, together with another substance, bryonidin. First symptoms are vomiting and diarrhoea with severe abdominal pain. A handful of berries can kill a child.

Calcium oxalates (*Arisaema triphyllum; Dieffenbachia* spp, No 6; *Symplocarpus foetidus*) They affect the mucous membranes of the mouth and produce intense burning and irritation. Fortunately this stops one eating the plant, thus preventing serious poisoning. Where they are soluble, as oxalates, and enter the blood stream, they can cause kidney damage. Oxalates combine with calcium in the blood and deposit in the bladder; coma results from the blood being starved of calcium in this way.

Cicutoxin (*Cicuta maculata*)   An unsaturated higher alcohol which affects the nervous system. Symptoms include salivation, vomiting, severe gastric pain, great mental excitation and frenzy, violent spasmodic convulsions, dilated pupils and delirium. They usually appear within thirty minutes, but death (due to paralysis and respiratory failure) has been known to occur within fifteen minutes of ingesting a lethal amount. Professional treatment usually involves gastric lavage and the use of such drugs as barbiturates and morphine.

Colchicine (*Colchicum autumnale*, No 1)   An alkaloid producing gastro-intestinal irritation and diarrhoea; the respiratory system may also be affected, with consequential coma and death.

Conium (*Conium maculatum*, No 70)   A volatile oil – a mixture of five deadly alkaloids, the most poisonous of which is coniine. Symptoms are creeping coldness and paralysis from the feet upwards, till death occurs through respiratory failure and depression of the brain's controlling function.

Convallamarin, convallarin (*Convallaria majalis*, No 2)   Cardiac glycosides causing heart stimulation similar to digitalis glycosides. Small amounts cause abdominal pain and purging with slower heart-beat, dizziness and vomiting. Larger doses affect the nervous system causing mental disturbance and convulsions.

Coumarin (*Aesculus hippocastanum*)   A toxic derivative of the glycoside aesculin, causing vomiting and diarrhoea. Can be fatal.

Cyanide   A simple chemical compound of one atom of carbon and one of nitrogen joined to a third. In nature, the latter is usually hydrogen, giving the form known as hydrogen cyanide gas (HCN). This form can be found in several substances such as amygdalin and other cyanogenetic glycosides.

Delphinine (*Delphinium ajacis*, No 5, related species and hybrids)   A polycyclic diterpene causing digestive upset, nervous excitement or depression. Can be fatal. Needs gastric lavage and professional treatment.

Digitalin, digitonin, digitoxin (*Digitalis purpurea*, No 7)   Cardiac glycosides, not to be confused with the compound drug digitalis, which is extracted from this plant. Large amounts of these glycosides cause dangerously irregular heartbeat, digestive upset, mental confusion, and can be fatal. Induced vomiting is recommended as a first-aid measure, followed by professional supportive treatment.

Euphorbin (*Euphorbia lathyris*, No 74)   A substance contained in the sap of all euphorbias and believed to be the cause of the symptoms of poisoning – lesions of the mouth and digestive system, gastroenteritis, diarrhoea.

Fagopyrin (*Fagopyrum sagittatum*, see p 182)   A chemical suspected to be the cause of allergic and photosensitive reactions in both humans and animals.

Gelsemine, gelseminine (*Gelsemium sempervirens*, No 12)   Toxic alkaloids which depress and paralyse the motor nerve endings. Depression of the brain neurons and of the spinal cord results in respiratory arrest. Professional treatment, including artificial respiration, is required.

Githagin (*Agrostemma githago*, No 57)   A saponin glycoside. Small amounts produce vomiting, diarrhoea and headache. Larger doses lead to convulsions, a breaking down of the red blood cells and death due to respiratory failure.

Helleborein, helleborin (*Hellebores*, Nos 15, 16)   Cardiac glycosides reputed to cause severe gastrointestinal upsets, leading to delirium, convulsions and even death.

Hyoscyamine (*Datura stramonium*, No 72; *Hyoscyamus niger*, No 80)   An alkaloid causing visual disturbance, rapid weak heartbeat, delirium, convulsions, coma and occasionally death.

Iridin (*Iris foetidissima*, Nos 19, 20; *I. versicolor*, No 22)   Acrid resinous substance which produces severe, although usually not serious, digestive upsets. It affects the gastrointestinal tracts, liver and pancreas, causing inflammation and diarrhoea. Cases of dermatitis have also been recorded. Professional treatment involves the use of such drugs as antihistamines and barbiturates.

Lantodene A (*Lantana camara*, No 25)   A polycyclic triterpenoid suspected of causing extreme muscular weakness, gastrointestinal irritation with pain and diarrhoea, failure of the circulatory system and, in serious cases, death. Vomiting should be induced prior to professional treatment.

Ligustrin (*Ligustrum vulgare*, No 27)   A glycoside, causes gastric upsets with vomiting and diarrhoea, and death in severe cases.

Mandragorin (*Mandragora officinarum*, No 84)   An alkaloid; according to some authors, a combination of hyoscyamine and scopolamine. It was once used as an anaesthetic, mixed with opium, henbane, lettuce and camphor. Symptoms of poisoning actually include loss of feeling and insensitivity to pain, followed by heavy sedation, coma and death.

Muscarine (*Amanita muscaria*, No 110)   An hallucinogenic and over-stimulant of the nervous system, it causes sweating, wheezing, irregular breathing and heart action, vomiting. The latter, often the first natural reaction, eliminates the poison from the organism before lethal doses can be absorbed.

Nerioside (*Nerium oleander*, No 31)   Cardiac glycoside (see oleandrin).

Oleandrin, Oleandroside (*Nerium oleander*, No 31)   Cardiac glycosides causing nausea, slow pulse, drowsiness, bloody diarrhoea, irregular heartbeat, unconsciousness and paralysis of the muscles controlling breathing. Can also produce dermatitis. Induced vomiting helps as a first aid, but treatment can only be professional.

Papaverine (*Papaver somniferum*, No 34)   One of the many alkaloids which are contained in the drug opium.

Phalloidin (*Amanita phalloides*, No 112)   A slow-acting toxin, the symptoms of which appear some 8–12 hours after ingestion and consist of severe abdominal pains, vomiting and diarrhoea, jaundice and cyanosis. Attacks are interspersed with deceptive periods of rest. The combined action of phalloidin (four times as potent as cyanide) and amanitine is usually fatal.

Ranunculin (*Ranunculus* spp.)   A glycoside found in the sap. It is the source of the highly irritant and vesicant oil protoanemonin. Ingestion causes severe gastroenteritis.

Ricin (*Ricinus communis*, No 43)   A phytotoxin, one of the most toxic substances known; can also cause allergenic reactions of great severity.

Very small doses (one or two seeds) have been known to be fatal. The first symptoms of burning in the mouth and throat are followed, within a few hours, by gastroenteritis with pain and diarrhoea, weakness of body and pulse, and fatal damage to kidneys and liver. Ricin coagulates the red blood cells and causes internal haemorrhages.

Robin, robitin (*Robinia pseudoacacia*, No 44) The former a toxin, the latter a glycoside. Symptoms include diarrhoea, vomiting, dilated pupils, irregular pulse and breathing difficulties.

Scopolamine (*Datura stramonium*, No 72) A toxic compound which at times has been used as a truth serum and (reportedly) as a brainwashing drug. Also found in the mandrake.

Solanaceous alkaloids, see stramonine.

Solanine (*Solanum dulcamara*, No 102) A glycoalkaloid which can only be treated symptomatically after gastric lavage. It causes burning of the throat, nausea, dizziness, dilation of the pupils, convulsions, muscular weakness, gastrointestinal irritation, anorexia, constipation and diarrhoea. Death results from paralysis, but ingestions are not always fatal.

Stramonine (*Datura stramonium*, No 72) A drug made of three separate compounds: hyoscyamine, atropine and scopolamine. Main symptoms include intense thirst, dilated pupils, vomiting, vertigo, partial blindness, weak pulse, delirium followed by hyperthermia, convulsions, coma and death.

Taxine (*Taxus baccata*, No 105) An alkaloid which depresses the heart function. First symptoms are nausea, diarrhoea, abdominal pain, circulatory failure and difficulty in breathing. Professional treatment includes gastric lavage and supportive drugs.

Tetrahydro-cannabinols (*Cannabis sativa*, No 67) A resinous mixture the effects of which vary with the individual and the dosage, but are very well known. Overdoses lead to depression and coma.

Tyramine (*Phoradendron flavescens*, No 91) One of the two active principles of this plant (the other being phenylethylamine), causing gastroenteritis and, in fatal cases, failure of the cardiovascular system.

POISONS AND THE HUMAN BODY

It must be pointed out first of all that a poison can kill a person even if it affects only one organ or one part of the body system. And secondly that, as has been stressed before, all reactions to poisons are variable, individual reactions depending on factors such as the efficiency of the poisoning process itself, the organs or tissues attacked, the condition of the human organism at the time of the poisoning (health, age, sex, emotional state, previous exposure, etc), the number of compounds making up the toxic substance and the way the poison enters the organism. The following shows what can happen to our body under the action of certain poisons.

1 Enzymes

An enzyme is a substance which has the property of changing one compound into another; one of them, for instance, uses water and other materials present in a cell to make sugar. The atomic structure of the enzymes, like that of proteins, is extremely complex and delicate, and easily destroyed by heat and by those substances which, for this reason, we call poisons.

Each enzyme carries out a different chemical reaction within the human cells; and some cells contain thousands of them. Some enzymes are represented in large quantities, others in tiny amounts; and some perform vital functions. One of them, cytochrome, uses the oxygen carried by the blood. Fifty milligrams of cyanide contain enough molecules to outnumber the body cells by about ten to one and destroy the cytochromes in them. The cells can then no longer use the oxygen carried by the blood and the organism suffocates.

2 The nervous system and the muscles

This is a highly complicated network of interconnected nerves which transmit the signals emitted by the brain to any part of the body, and control the movements of the muscles.

Physiologically, the nervous system is divided into voluntary and involuntary (autonomic). The latter controls the heart, the internal organs and the glands with a two-way system – the sympathetic system which stimulates the muscles to contract more strongly or frequently, and the parasympathetic which reduces such contractions. Both can be affected by poisons acting on either and, by their nature, can be subjected to opposite and counteracting stimuli which play further havoc with this delicate communications network. The whole system is rendered more complex by the fact that each brain message is not transmitted directly, but from one nerve to another; and by the existence of a gap between the nerves or between a nerve-ending and a muscle. To understand the effects of poisons on the nervous system, one must appreciate the following details of what happens in this gap.

The nerve-ending both produces and stores tiny particles of acetylcholine which, ruptured by the nerve impulse, flow into the gap and attach themselves to the muscle membrane, thus transmitting the impulse itself. They would go on doing so indefinitely, with imaginable results, were it not for the enzyme cholinesterase. This enzyme is liberated by the muscle's cells specifically to annihilate the acetylcholine and restore peace. The entire process lasts for about 1/500 of a second. But poisons can interfere with this process. Curare, for instance, blocks the nerve impulse by coating the muscle membrane, and prevents any brain message whatever from reaching the muscle; an overdose can cause death by suffocation. Other poisons can dampen or altogether block the cholinesterase, thus causing a build-up of acetylcholine in the gap and the continuous stimulation of the muscle.

3 Respiratory system

We all know the function of the ducts which conduct air through the nose, trachea and bronchi down to the lungs; the sponge-like structure of the latter making a very large surface available for the exchange between the carbon dioxide carried by the blood and the oxygen inhaled. The contraction and expansion of the lungs is controlled and determined by the contraction and expansion of the muscles which control the diaphragm and the chest under stimuli imparted by the autonomic nervous system. Clearly, any poison which impaires the functioning of the nervous system can seriously affect respiration.

Allergies, such as asthma, affect the diameter of the air passages themselves and consequently the supply of oxygen to the blood. Nerve impulses from the brain affect respiration, as do those from other parts of the body such as nose and throat. That is why vomiting under the influence of a poison can result in the blockage of the air passages to the lungs.

4 Circulatory system

A very vulnerable system indeed, as most ingested poisons get absorbed into the blood vessels and circulate to the various parts of the body together with foodstuffs, waste products, hormones, chemicals and oxygen. The very heartbeat, which keeps the blood in circulation, is in turn affected by this flow – the larger the amount of venous blood returning to the heart, the quicker the contractions of the heart muscles; on the other hand, the heartbeat slows down and blood pressure falls when increasing amounts of arterial blood reach the muscles. Vice versa, the output of blood from the heart is affected by changes in the heartbeat, both in frequency and in strength. And both blood flow and heartbeat can be affected by changes in the walls of the capillaries at the periphery of the circulatory system, such as may occur in cases of allergy.

So much for the mechanics of it. What about the substances, essential to our well-being, which circulate with the blood? We have seen how cyanide prevents the body from using up oxygen by destroying the enzyme cytochrome. Other poisons affect the adrenalin – the hormone which controls the heartbeat – as well as other vital chemicals.

The clotting of blood, a very complex chemical process in itself, can also be affected by certain toxic substances found in plants. Some of these prevent the clotting altogether (for instance by destroying the calcium present in the blood) and cause haemorrhages; others cause the blood cells to agglutinate and others still break them down altogether.

5 Digestive system

Before any of the foodstuffs we eat can be of any use to us, they must be properly dealt with; for only well-digested food can be absorbed into the blood system and circulated to the organs in need of it. This digestive process begins in the mouth, where the food is broken down, fairly roughly, by mastication and by the enzymes contained in the saliva – as my grandmother never failed to remind us, thus making us lose what little appetite we had as children!

From the mouth the food moves down the oesophagus and passes into the stomach via the cardiac sphincter. Here it gets mixed with the gastric juices which break it down further. Very few substances pass straight from the stomach walls into the blood; one of them is alcohol, others are water and sugars. The rest pass into the small intestine through the pyloric sphincter; hence more nutrients and enzymes are released into the blood and conveyed to the liver or to other parts of the organism. Contractions of the muscles in the intestine walls move the residues along into the large intestine, where water and salts are removed for storage, and what is left is prepared for expulsion. Any upset at any stage of this process, any alteration to the amount of water and nutrients extracted from the food, to the extent of the digestion itself and to the speed at which the food is processed, can contribute to either diarrhoea or constipation – both very common in cases of plant poisoning.

The other common symptom is vomiting, which occurs when nerve impulses from the affected part of the system, even from the stomach itself, cause the pyloric sphincter to close, the pyloric area to contract and the diaphragm and abdominal muscles to compress the abdominal cavity thus expelling the stomach contents. Vomiting may occur immediately after the ingestion of a poison, thus reducing the chances of the toxic substance being absorbed into the blood stream. Many plant poisons, however, need to be modified by the enzymes in the intestine before they develop their toxicity to the full. This part of the digestive system contains several micro-organisms which are normally beneficial to our health and which are very vulnerable to attack from other microbes or from the wrong chemicals; their destruction causes the digestive upsets often found in cases of plant poisoning.

6 Other internal organs

We have seen how the brain, the heart, the lungs, the stomach and the intestines can be affected by the ingestion of toxic substances. Let us now have a look at two more vital organs – the liver and the kidneys.

The liver is one of the most important organs, being a combination of chemical factory, energy store and sewage-treatment plant. It secretes the chemicals which aid the digestive process; it converts glucose into glycogen and stores it until needed; it alters the nutrients produced by the digestive process into substances which can be used by specific organs and functions; and it detoxifies the harmful substances we ingest in the course of *normal* nutrition. Furthermore, it has a built-in reserve of cells which are endowed with the most potent regenerative powers in the human body.

But the liver is not invulnerable. It is controlled by the autonomic nervous system, and anything which harms this system seriously affects the liver's functions. It is also the first line of defence against toxic chemicals and some of them prove to be too potent for it to handle. Many plant substances passed on from the digestive system via the blood stream can damage the liver to such an extent that both these and other substances, normally detoxified without problems, are allowed to re-circulate and do their worst. The damage caused by these substances to the liver can be immediately fatal or can progress over a certain period. In the latter case, the toxins can make their way to other organs and cause more harm, again with serious or fatal consequences.

The kidneys are filters *par excellence*. The blood deposits within them water, salts and other waste products, at the same time reabsorbing certain nutrients. All the various syntheses of waste products which take place in the kidneys can be affected by the toxic substances which circulate in the blood in cases of plant poisoning. Amanitine, as we have already seen, is one such substance.

HOW TO READ THE SYMBOLS

cm	m
90	9
80	8
70	7
60	6
50	5
40	4
30	3
20	2
10	1

Plant height
Scales from 0–90cm and from 0–9m: indicating the minimum and maximum height a given plant can reach. Heights above 9m are indicated in the text.

Poisonous period
Roman figures: indicating the months of the year when the plant or fungus must be considered poisonous.

I	II	III	IV	V	VI	VII	VIII	IX	X	XI	XII

Habitat

 Meadows, hedgerows

 Moorlands, wastelands

 Parks, gardens, special cultivations

 Woodland

 Pastures, cultivated fields

 Peatbogs and marshes

 Water-side, river or lake banks

 Mountains, rocky highlands, cliffs

 Cultivated in greenhouses or indoors

 Found growing wild

Identifying the plant

Position of leaves on the plant
Rosette: leaves arranged at the base of the plant in variously shaped rosettes

Alternate or spiral: leaves growing on the stem at different levels

 Opposed: leaves growing in pairs on the same level and opposite

 Verticillate: more than two leaves growing at the same level around the stem or branch or at the tip of it

 Imbricated: leaves growing over one another, in well-defined order

Shape of leaves

 Narrow leaf

 Broad leaf, oval to lanceolate

 Single leaf with more or less incised margin or lobes

 Single leaf indented almost to the centre in the shape of a fan

 Composite leaf formed by variously shaped folioles attached to the same axis

Inflorescence
Plant without flowers: ferns, mosses

 Single flower

 Raceme or cluster

Spike, or alternate on stem, or axillary

 Amentum

 Corymb

 Umbel

 Flat capitulum

 Cyme, panicle

 Scorpioid cyme

Poisonous parts of the plant

 Flowers and buds

  Seeds

 Leaves

 Roots, bulb, rhizome

 Fruit

 Stem, bark or sap

 Whole plant may be poisonous

Identifying the fungi
Cap

 Concave

 Convex

Umbonate

 Campanulate, bell-shaped or conical

 Gibbous (ie with humps)

 Warty

Squamous or fibrillose

 Scaly

 Areolate

 Velvety

 Viscid or glutinous, particularly in wet weather

 Zonal (ie with more or less concentric stripes)

 Hygrophanous (changing colour in wet weather)

 Fleshy

 Thin

 Globular

 On trunks, boles and woody remains

Humans most at risk
Children

Adults

Severity of attack
Mild

 Severe

 Possibly fatal

Treatment
close surveillance and symptomatic treatment

 Prevent further absorption of poison by inducing vomiting if patient is conscious

 Seek medical aid and give artificial respiration if necessary

Dermatitis
Causes skin irritation and other allergic reactions

Duration of symptoms

 Short term

 Long term

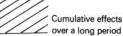 Cumulative effects over a long period

Autumn crocus

Liliaceae

Description: large linear leaves in spring die back before the flower appears in autumn; flowers tubular, pale purple/mauve; fruits, ovoid, in spring, with many seeds; corms covered in brown scales.
Active principles: colchicine and other alkaloids resistant to boiling or drying.
Symptoms: abdominal pain and burning; diarrhoea, weakness, difficult breathing, convulsions; coma and respiratory failure may occur. Cattle may graze it and pass the toxins on in milk.
Treatment: professional.

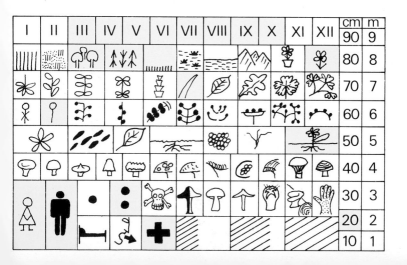

Lily of the valley   Liliaceae

Description: perennial; creeping roots; leaves in pairs; flowers on leafless stalks, white, bell-shaped, attractively scented; fruits: red berries with several seeds.
Active principles: cardiac glycosides (convallarin, convallamarin).
Symptoms: small quantities: abdominal pain, diarrhoea, slowing of heartbeat; larger quantities: mental disturbance, convulsions, occasionally death.
Treatment: symptomatic/professional.

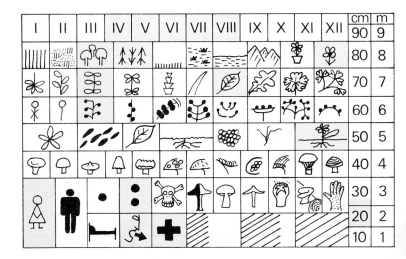

Mezereon
Thymelaeaceae

Description: deciduous shrub; leaves entire, obovate; flowers purple/pink, fragrant, appearing before the leaves; fruits round, yellowish to scarlet.

Active principles: primary irritant, mezerein, coumarin glycoside (stable).

Symptoms: external: blisters; internal: burning and ulceration of mouth and stomach, swelling of mucous membranes; nausea, vomiting, diarrhoea; delirium; collapse and death can occur in serious cases (10–12 berries).

Treatment: give emetic and seek professional help.

4 *Daphne cneorum* L.

Garland flower
Thymelaeaceae

Description: evergreen spreading shrublet; highly scented flowers, red or pink; leaves clustered at end of hairy branchlets; fruits orange.
Active principles, Symptoms and Treatment: as *D. mezereum.*

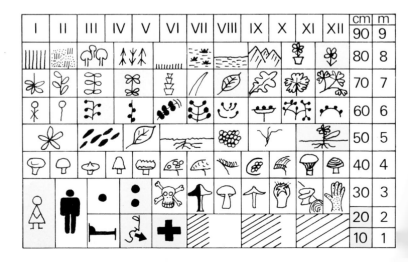

I	II	III	IV	V	VI	VII	VIII	IX	X	XI	XII	cm	m
												90	9
												80	8
												70	7
												60	6
												50	5
												40	4
												30	3
												20	2
												10	1

Larkspur

Ranunculaceae

Description: erect annual; straight taproot; leaves divided into long, narrow segments; flowers blue, white, pink, terminal and spurred; many-seeded fruit capsules.
Active principles: alkaloids (delphinine), presenting seasonal variations.
Symptoms: constipation, nausea, vomiting, paralysis of limbs, difficult breathing, irregular heartbeat; deadly.
Treatment: professional.

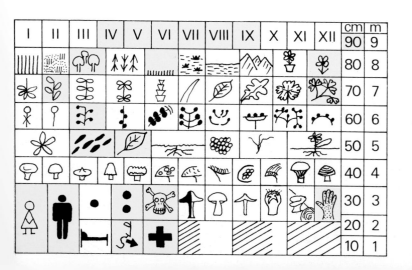

Dumb cane

Araceae

Description: evergreen ornamentals; the various species and varieties in this genus make familar houseplants (*D. amoena, D. picta, D. candida, D. seguine*).
Active principles: toxic substances including calcium oxalates.
Symptoms: burning and irritation of mouth and tongue, swelling affecting swallowing and breathing.
Treatment: symptomatic.

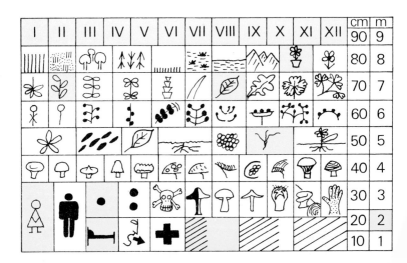

Foxglove
Scrophulariaceae

Description: erect biennial; leaves hairy, ovate/lanceolate; flowers pinkish/purple, often spotted inside; fruit: capsules with several tiny seeds.

Active principles: stable cardiac glycosides (digitalin, digitoxin) and alkaloids.

Symptoms: vomiting, diarrhoea, slow and strong heartbeat, mental disturbance, convulsions; death may occur.

Treatment: symptomatic/professional.

I	II	III	IV	V	VI	VII	VIII	IX	X	XI	XII	cm	m
												90	9
												80	8
												70	7
												60	6
												50	5
												40	4
												30	3
												20	2
												10	1

Wild hyacinth, Bluebell
Liliaceae

Description: bulbous perennial, leafless flower stem; flowers blue/white; fruits green with black seeds.
Active principles: unidentified.
Symptoms: abdominal pain, diarrhoea, bloody urine.
Treatment: symptomatic/professional.

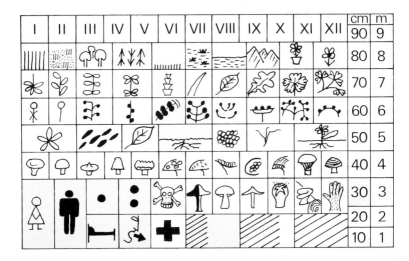

Poinsettia

Euphorbiaceae

Syn. *Poinsettia pulcherrima* R. Grah.

Description: perennial shrub; leaves with entire, toothed or lobed margins; upper leaves forming bright red, pink or white bracts; flowers tiny in tight groups; appearing in winter. Bright bracts are partciularly attractive to children.
Active principles: euphorbin.
Symptoms: sap causes blistering of skin; ingestion leads to vomiting, diarrhoea, delirium.
Treatment: professional

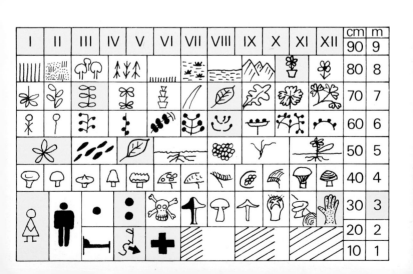

Snake's head fritillary
Liliaceae

Description: bulbous perennial; solitary bell-shaped flowers, chequered; upper leaves linear; fruits globose.
Active principles: bulb: alkaloids (possibly in all parts).
Symptoms: depressant of heart. No recently reported cases.
Treatment: professional.

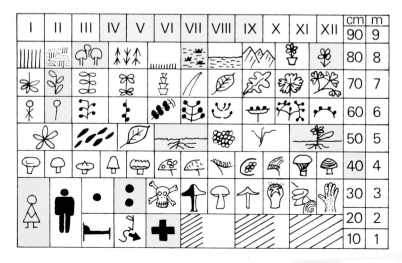

Yellow jessamine

Loganiaceae

Description: evergreen perennial vine; fragrant, tubular flowers, yellow, in clusters; fruits: flat capsules with winged seeds.
Active principles: alkaloids.
Symptoms: depression, double vision, weakness; death by respiratory failure.
Treatment: professional.

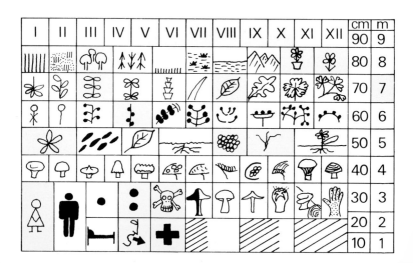

Glory lily, Climbing lily

Liliaceae

Description: climbing perennial, tuberous root; leaves lanceolate with tendril-like tips; yellow or red flowers; fruits: capsules.
Active principles: alkaloids.
Symptoms: abdominal pain, diarrhoea; can be fatal.
Treatment: symptomatic; professional in severe cases.

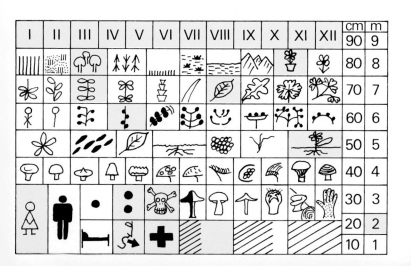

14 *Hedera helix* **L.**

Common ivy
Araliaceae

Description: climbing perennial, up to 35m, with adventitious roots; leaves glossy, evergreen, lobed when young, entire later; flowers small, greenish; berries round, black.
Active principles: saponin, hederin, hederagenin; formic and malic acids, colesterin, pectine.
Symptoms: sap may cause dermatitis; ingestion of berries leads to strong purgation, in large quantities to vomiting, diarrhoea, coma.
Treatment: symptomatic (emetics) except in serious cases.

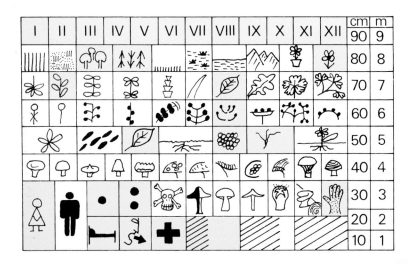

Stinking hellebore

Ranunculaceae

Description: erect perennial, branching stems; lower leaves evergreen, palmate: upper leaves entire and ovate; flowers greenish, globular (Feb–Apr).
Active principles: stable cardiac glycosides (helleborin, helleborein).
Symptoms: gastrointestinal; purging, weakness, delirium, convulsions; death from respiratory failure.
Treatment: professional.

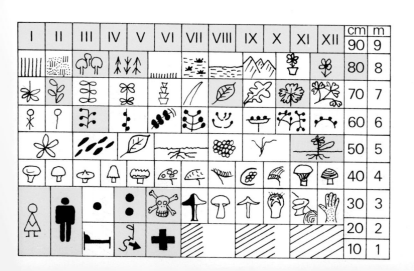

16 *Helleborus niger* L.

Black hellebore, Christmas rose   Ranunculaceae

Description: perennial; fleshy black rhizome; leaves dark, glossy, toothed; flowers white/pink (Dec–Feb); seeds black, shiny.
Active principles: cardiac glycosides (helleborin, helleborein).
Symptoms: purging, vomiting, weakness, delirium, convulsions; death from respiratory failure.
Treatment: professional; no specific antidote.

Hydrangea, Hortensia

Saxifragaceae

Description: perennial, deciduous shrub; leaves coarsely toothed; flowers pink, blue, mauve. Can grow wild, as garden escape, in hot climates.
Active principles: cyanogenetic glycosides.
Symptoms: gastroenteritis with pain, nausea, diarrhoea.
Treatment: symptomatic.

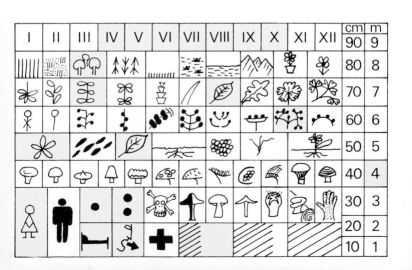

Morning glory

Convolvulaceae

Description: twining annual; hairy stems; leaves entire; flowers funnel-shaped in leaf axils; fruits: capsules. Many forms are cultivated.
Active principles: hallucinogens (amides of lysergic acid); alkaloids (argine, isoergine and others chemically related to LSD).
Symptoms: unpredictable psychological disturbances, including heightened perception of vision, smell and hearing; can cause permanent damage to brain, and death.
Treatment: professional.

I	II	III	IV	V	VI	VII	VIII	IX	X	XI	XII	cm	m
												90	9
												80	8
												70	7
												60	6
												50	5
												40	4
												30	3
												20	2
												10	1

Stinking iris

Iridaceae

Description: perennial rhizomatous; leaves evergreen in tufts; flowers purplish violet; fruit: capsules with bright orange-red seeds.
Active principles: iridin (glycoside).
Symptoms: gastroenteritis; keep berries from children. Whole plant poisonous to livestock and pets.
Treatment: symptomatic/professional.

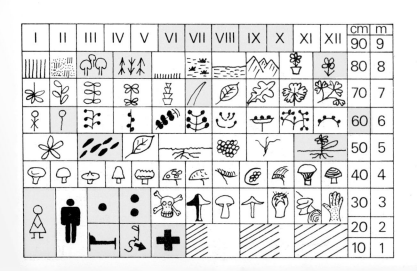

Stinking iris
Seed pods

Iridaceae

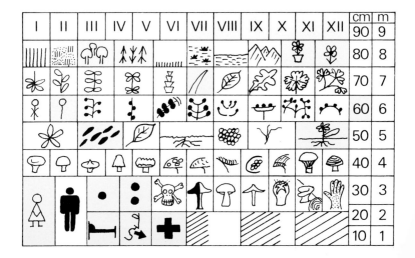

Yellow flag

Iridaceae

Description: rhizomatous perennial; leaves sheathing stem at base; flowers yellow or cream; fruit green with several brown seeds.
Active principles: iridin (glycoside).
Symptoms: vomiting, severe purgation (dangerous to animals).
Treatment: symptomatic.

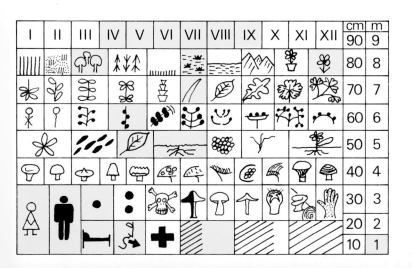

22 *Iris versicolor* L.

Purple flag   Iridaceae

Description: perennial, clump-forming, rhizomatous; branching flower stems carrying several flowers; flowers violet/purplish blue/purplish red; fruits: capsules with several seeds.

Active principles, Symptoms and Treatment: as *I. foetidissima*.

I	II	III	IV	V	VI	VII	VIII	IX	X	XI	XII	cm	m
												90	9
												80	8
												70	7
												60	6
												50	5
												40	4
												30	3
												20	2
												10	1

Calico bush

Ericaceae

Description: dense evergreen shrub; flowers white to pink, bell-shaped; fruits: capsules with many seeds.
Active principles: andromedotoxin, arbutin (glycoside).
Symptoms: gastrointestinal; vomiting, pain; weakness, breathing difficulties; can be fatal.
Treatment: professional.

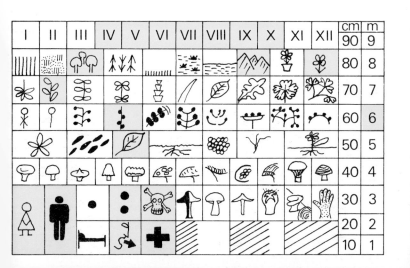

Laburnum
Papilionaceae

Description: tree up to 10m high; deciduous; leaves trifoliate; flowers yellow, in hanging racemes; fruit pods with dark brown kidney-shaped seeds.

Active principles: cytisine (alkaloid).

Symptoms: vomiting, stomach pain, convulsions and incoordination, coma and death from asphyxia; seeds are highly dangerous to children (15 can be fatal); bark, leaves and flowers have also caused poisoning.

Treatment: professional; first aid: emetics and artificial respiration.

I	II	III	IV	V	VI	VII	VIII	IX	X	XI	XII	cm	m
												90	9
												80	8
												70	7
												60	6
												50	5
												40	4
												30	3
												20	2
												10	1

Lantana (cultivated form)

Verbenaceae

Description: perennial shrub; stems square, with spines; leaves smell strongly when crushed; flowers tubular in dense clusters; fruits blackish with one seed.
Active principles: lantodene (polycyclic terpenoid).
Symptoms: gastrointestinal: pain, diarrhoea; weakness, circulatory failure; death can occur in serious cases.
Treatment: professional.

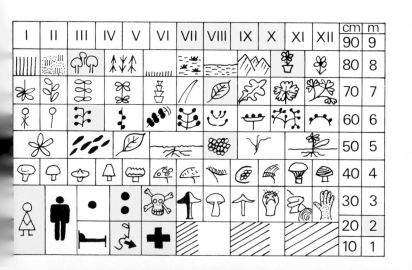

26 *Lathyrus odoratus* L.

Sweet pea
Papilionaceae

Description: annual
climber; pointed leaflets;
flowers bluish/white/pink
(several colours in
cultivated hybrids); fruits
oblong and hairy.
Active principles: beta-
amino-propionitrile.
Symptoms: spastic
paraplegia, convulsions,
paralysis of the larynx
(lathyrism).
Treatment: professional.

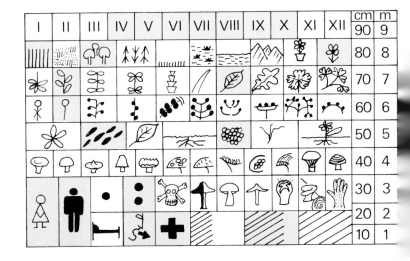

Common privet

Oleaceae

Description: perennial evergreen shrub, widely used for hedges; flowers small, white; berries purple-black.
Active principles: ligustrin (glycoside).
Symptoms: gastric irritation, vomiting, diarrhoea.
Treatment: emetics; symptomatic.

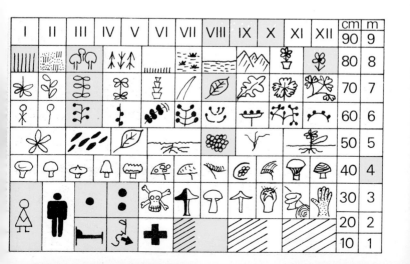

Lupin
Seed pods

Papilionaceae

Description: annual/perennial; leaves digitate on stalks; flowers various colours; fruit pods hairy with up to 6 seeds.
Active principles: stable alkaloids. Toxicity variable from species to species and year to year.
Symptoms: variable, mainly depression of respiratory and circulatory systems; dangerous to children and livestock.
Treatment: symptomatic/professional.

I	II	III	IV	V	VI	VII	VIII	IX	X	XI	XII	cm	m
												90	9
												80	8
												70	7
												60	6
												50	5
												40	4
												30	3
												20	2
												10	1

Four-o'clock   Nyctaginaceae

Description: shrubby herbaceous, native of tropics; flowers surrounded by coloured bracts open in evening and can be white, yellow or red; fruits: achenes with one seed.
Active principles: trigonelline (alkaloid).
Symptoms: external: irritation of skin and mucous membranes; internal: gastrointestinal upsets, diarrhoea.
Treatment: symptomatic.

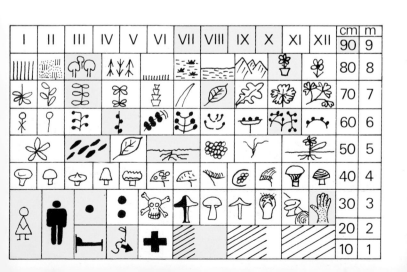

Daffodil   Amaryllidaceae

Description: bulbous perennial; upright stalk; upright to horizontal flower, shades of yellow. Cultivated forms can be double and in various shades. Fruit: capsule.
Active principles: toxic alkaloids.
Symptoms: severe gastroenteritis, vomiting; possibly convulsions.
Treatment: symptomatic/professional.

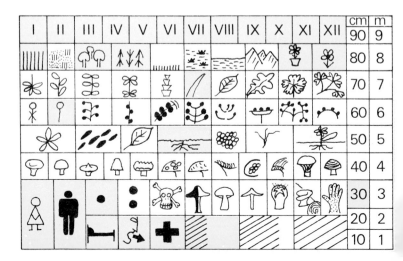

Oleander

Apocynaceae

Description: evergreen shrub; leaves entire, lanceolate; dark green above. Flowers white, pink or purplish; fruits: hanging pods.
Active principles: oleandrin, oleandroside, nerioside (cardiac glycosides).
Symptoms: severe gastroenteritis, drowsiness, quickening of heartbeat, abdominal pain followed by breathing difficulties, weak heartbeat, coma and death within 24 hours.
Treatment: professional.

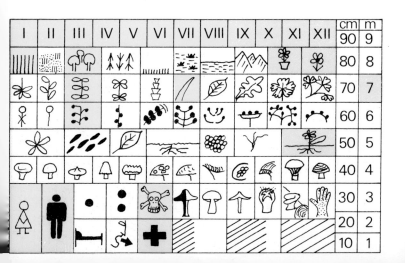

Tobacco
Solanaceae

Description: annual;
leaves up to 60cm long;
flowers pink; fruits:
capsules with several
brown seeds.
Active principles:
alkaloids (nicotine).
Symptoms: nicotine is
readily absorbed through
skin and results can be
fatal (see *Conium
maculatum*, No 70).
Treatment: professional.

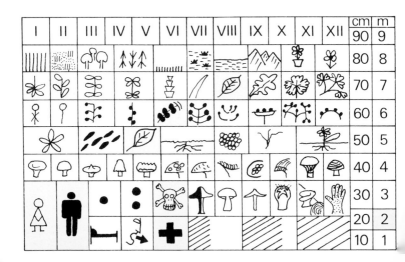

Iceland poppy

Papaveraceae

Description: perennial; glaucous leaves; flowers orange to yellow; capsules oblong, hairy.
Active principles: unidentified.
Symptoms: drowsiness; gastrointestinal disturbances (dangerous to livestock).
Treatment: symptomatic.

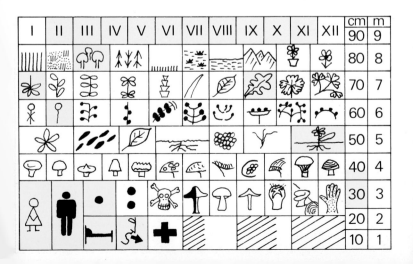

Opium poppy
Papaveraceae

Description: annual
herb; taproot; leaves with
irregular lobes, glaucous;
flowers whitish lilac,
occasionally with dark
blotches; capsules
globular, ovoid; seeds
tiny, black or white.
Active principles:
isoquinoline alkaloids
(morphine, codeine,
papaverine, narcotine) in
sap.
Symptoms: depression of
central nervous system;
headache, giddiness,
vomiting, drowsiness,
weakness; irregular
breathing and coma in
severe cases.
Treatment: professional.

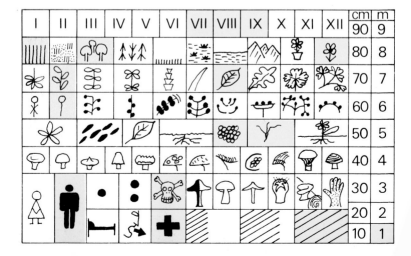

Virginia creeper

Vitaceae

Syn. *Ampelopsis quinquefolia* Mich.

Description: deciduous perennial climber (10m and above); branched tendrils; toothed obovate leaflets (5 per leaf); flowers small, greenish; berries black.
Active principles: unidentified.
Symptoms: gastrointestinal.
Treatment: professional.

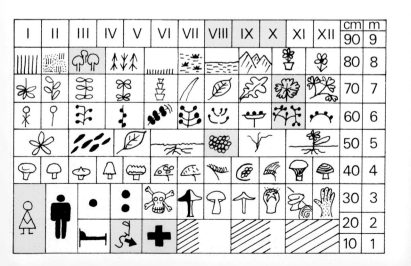

Chinese lantern
Solanaceae

Description: herbaceous
perennial; leaves petiolate,
irregular; flowers white;
fruits contained within
orange-red inflated calyx,
red or orange; seeds
yellow.
Active principles:
physalin, alkaloids.
Symptoms:
gastrointestinal; irritation
of urinary system.
Treatment:
symptomatic.

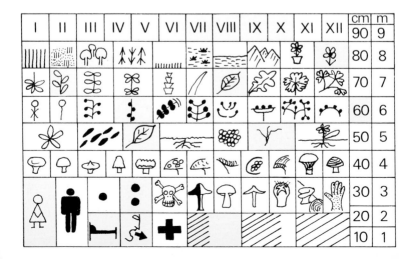

Bird of Paradise, Poinciana

Leguminosae

Description: shrub to small tree, native to South America; compound leaves with oblong leaflets; flowers light yellow; green pods.
Active principles: unidentified.
Symptoms: gastroenteritis with vomiting and diarrhoea.
Treatment: symptomatic.

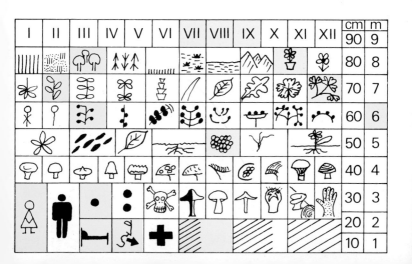

38 *Polygonatum officinale* All.

Solomon's seal

Liliaceae

Description: perennial, tuberous, creeping rootstock; flowers bell-shaped, pale; blue-black berries.
Active principles: anthraquinone.
Symptoms: nausea, abdominal pain, vomiting.
Treatment: symptomatic/professional.

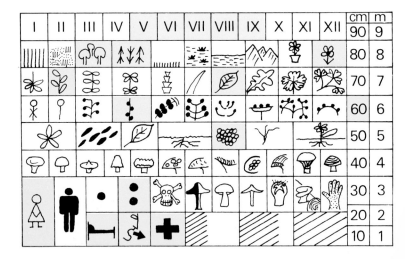

Pasque flower

Ranunculaceae

Description: perennial; leaves hairy, divided; flower violet purple; fruit: achene with plumed style.
Active principles: protoanemonin.
Symptoms: dermatitis from bruised leaves; gastrointestinal if ingested.
Treatment: symptomatic.

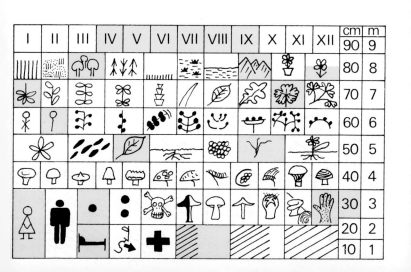

Cherry laurel
Rosaceae

Description: evergreen
shrub; leaves thick and
shiny; dark green above;
flowers white, axillary;
fruits: shiny, bluish to
black, one seed each. Used
for hedging.
Active principles:
cyanogenetic glycosides.
Symptoms: convulsions,
respiratory failure may
precede death, but
symptoms do not
necessarily show.
Treatment: professional.

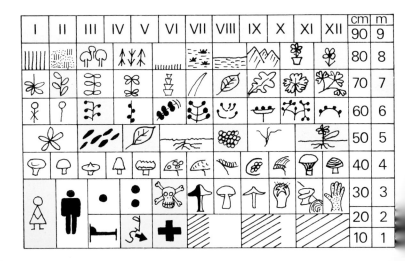

I	II	III	IV	V	VI	VII	VIII	IX	X	XI	XII	cm	m
												90	9
												80	8
												70	7
												60	6
												50	5
												40	4
												30	3
												20	2
												10	1

Rhubarb   Polygonaceae

Description: perennial; leaves large on long green to red stalks; flowers on hollow, branched stem, greenish white; fruit cordate, winged.
Active principles: oxalic acid, soluble oxalates.
Symptoms: vomiting, abdominal pain, diarrhoea, weakness; can be fatal.
Treatment: professional.

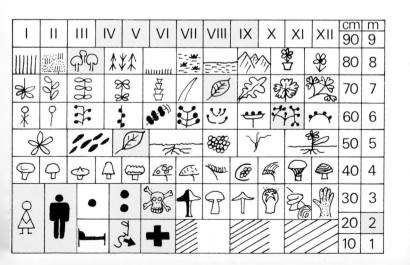

Rhododendron

Ericaceae

Description: large evergreen shrub; leaves dark upperside, pale or brown underside; flowers terminal, dull purple.
Active principles: andromedotoxin.
Symptoms: vomiting, vertigo, delirium.
Treatment: professional.

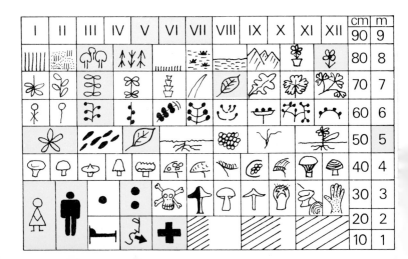

Ricinus communis L.   43

Castor bean
Euphorbiaceae

Description: annual; leaves on long stalks; sometimes found as herbaceous tree up to 13m high; flowers on lower parts; fruits: spiny capsules, seeds grey, mottled brown. Cultivated forms vary in details of foliage and fruits.

Active principles: seeds: ricin (phytotoxin).

Symptoms: has caused extremely serious allergenic reactions; just a few seeds chewed as laxative have proved fatal. Burning of mouth and throat is followed by diarrhoea, abdominal pain, cramps, weakness, haemorrhages, and damage to liver and kidneys.

Treatment: professional.

I	II	III	IV	V	VI	VII	VIII	IX	X	XI	XII	cm	m
												90	9
												80	8
												70	7
												60	6
												50	5
												40	4
												30	3
												20	2
												10	1

Black locust, Robinia
Leguminosae

Description: deciduous tree up to 10m; thorny young branches; leaves, 3 to 10 pairs of elliptical leaflets; flowers white or pink, scented; fruits: long pods with many seeds. Common in warmer parts of Europe.
Active principles: robin (toxin), robitin (glycoside).
Symptoms: vomiting, diarrhoea, weak pulse, difficult breathing.
Treatment: professional.

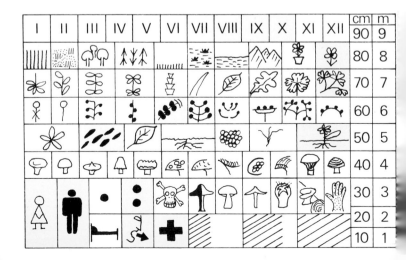

Stonecrop
Crassulaceae

Description: succulent
plant with several stems,
creeping or erect; fleshy
leaves, sometimes
imbricated; flowers
yellow; fruits: capsules
with oval seeds. Common
on old walls.
Active principles: rutin,
sedidrin.
Symptoms: externally,
can cause skin irritation;
internally, nausea,
diarrhoea.
Treatment:
symptomatic.

I	II	III	IV	V	VI	VII	VIII	IX	X	XI	XII	cm	m
												90	9
												80	8
												70	7
												60	6
												50	5
												40	4
												30	3
												20	2
												10	1

Chalice vine, Trumpet flower

Solanaceae

Description: branched climber; flowers yellow, fragrant, funnel-shaped; fruits globular, yellowish.
Active principles: solanine alkaloids.
Symptoms: headache, weakness, hallucinations and delirium, high temperature; circulatory and respiratory failure has led to death.
Treatment: professional.

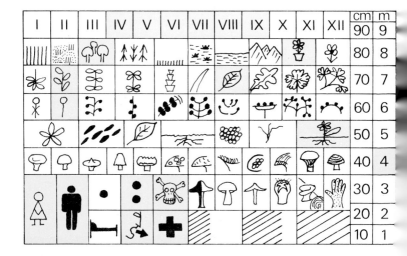

Potato   Solanaceae

Description: annual, fleshy stems; paired alternating leaves; flowers white; fruits globular yellowish green.
Active principles: solanine (alkaloid), particularly in green sprouting tubers.
Symptoms: gastrointestinal; drowsiness, weakness, breathing difficulties; green or sprouting tubers have been fatal to man and livestock.
Treatment: symptomatic/professional.

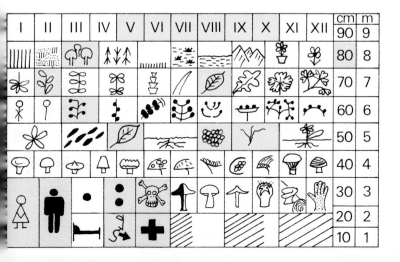

Snowberry   Caprifoliaceae

Description: deciduous shrub; petiolate leaves; flowers small, whitish, terminal; fruits: white berries.
Active principles: saponin and irritants.
Symptoms: can irritate skin; internally, gastroenteritis, vomiting, diarrhoea; can be severe.
Treatment: symptomatic/professional.

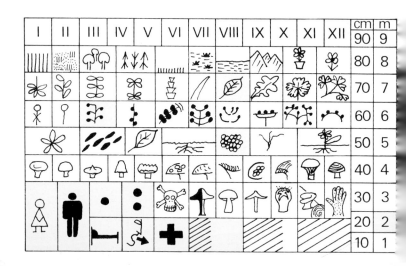

Guelder rose

Caprifoliaceae

Description: shrub; petiolate leaves; terminal white flowers; shiny red berries.
Active principles: viburnin, saponin.
Symptoms: gastrointestinal irritation, vomiting, diarrhoea, collapse; can be fatal.
Treatment: professional.

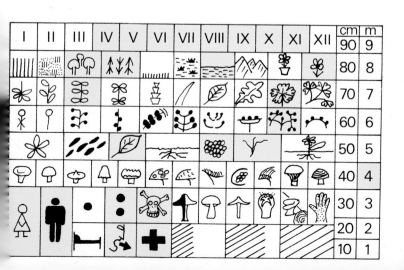

50 *Wistaria floribunda* DC.

Japanese wistaria
Leguminosae

Description: woody shrub trained on walls and pergolas; young branches twining; up to 19 ovate leaflets; flowers white, pink, blue, purple; hairy pods.
Active principles: resins and glycosides (wisterin).
Symptoms: gastrointestinal: vomiting, diarrhoea, pain; dehydration.
Treatment: symptomatic/professional.

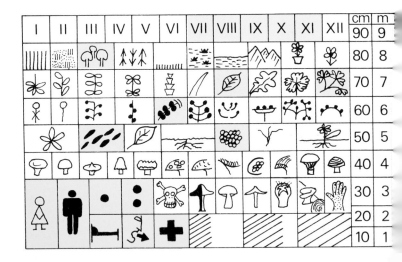

Chinese wistaria
Leguminosae

Description: commonly cultivated and similar to *W. floribunda*; flowers blue/violet.
Active principles, Symptoms and Treatment: as *W. floribunda*.

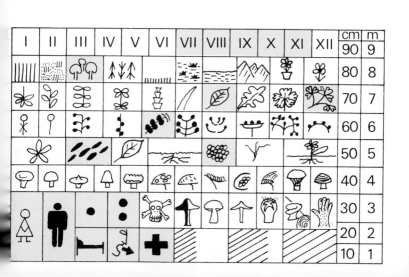

52 *Achillea millefolium* L.

Yarrow, Milfoil
Compositae

Description: perennial;
flowers white or pink in
corymbs; leaves deeply
indented.
Active principles:
achillein (glycoside),
tannin, asparagine,
phytosterine, resins.
Symptoms: allergic
reaction when crushed on
skin.
Treatment:
symptomatic.

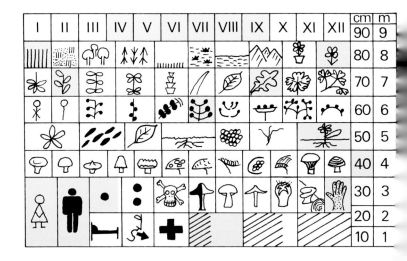

Monkshood, Aconite
Ranunculaceae

Description: perennial; leaves, deeply cut lobes (narrower in wild forms) with additional subdivisions; flowers, hooded, blue-mauve in wild forms.

Active principles: aconitine (alkaloid), aconitic acid.

Symptoms: immediate tingling of mouth and skin; restlessness, slow pulse, incoordination, vomiting, diarrhoea, convulsions; death by respiratory failure (up to 8 hours).

Treatment: induce vomit, give activated carbon, hospitalise for supportive treatment.

Red baneberry

Ranunculaceae

Description: perennial with stout dark rhizome; leaves biternate with serrated edges; flowers white; berries red.
Active principles: probably a glycoside and an essential oil.
Symptoms: quickening of heartbeat, gastroenteritis, dizziness, diarrhoea and vomiting.
Treatment: professional as it can be fatal.

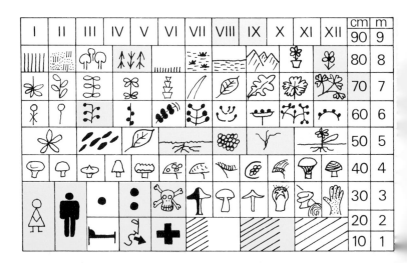

Baneberry, Herb Christopher

Ranunculaceae

Description: perennial herb; blackish rhizome; leaves biternate or bipinnate with ovate/3 lobed leaflets; flowers terminal, white; berries oval, green to blackish; seeds semi-circular, flattened.

Active principles: toxic essential oil; protoanemonin?

Symptoms: severe gastroenteritis, vomiting, diarrhoea, delirium; cases of death have been recorded; can cause skin blisters.

Treatment: usually symptomatic; professional depending on quantities.

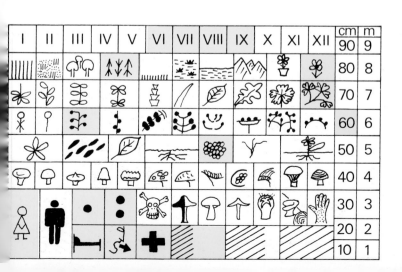

Fool's parsley, Lesser hemlock   Umbelliferae

Description: annual herb; hollow stems with pinnatifid segmented leaves; flowers tiny and pale with bracts; fruits ovoid. Leaves can be mistaken for parsley. Nauseous smell when rubbed.
Active principles: alkaloids; probably coniine (see *Conium maculatum*, No 70).
Symptoms: as *Conium maculatum*, although seldom fatal.
Treatment: induce vomit; seek medical attention if symptoms persist.

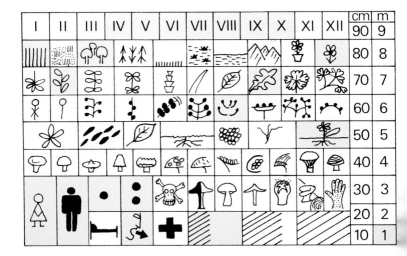

Corn cockle
Caryophyllaceae

Description: tall annual
weed, long hairy leaves,
reddish flowers, common
in wheatfields.
Active principles:
githagin, saponin
glycosides.
Symptoms: like gastroenteritis; lethal in large
doses.
Treatment: professional.

Wood anemone

Ranunculaceae

Description: perennial; basal leaves appear after flowering; flowers white to pale pink; achenes.

Active principles: anemonin, protoanemonin.

Symptoms: externally: possible irritation of the skin; internally: gastrointestinal, giddiness, cerebral irritation, failure of circulatory and respiratory systems.

Treatment: symptomatic; professional in severe cases.

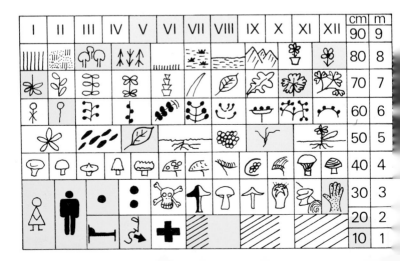

Columbine
Ranunculaceae

Description: perennial;
compound leaves, flowers
bluish/violet, drooping;
fruits, pods with several
small seeds.
Active principles:
glycosides originating
cyanidric acid.
Symptoms: similar to
Aconitum napellus (No 53).
Treatment: professional.

Arnica

Compositae

Description: herbaceous perennial with horizontal rhizome; flowers yellow.
Active principles: rhizome: arnicine (resinous compound), tannin and gallic acids; flowers: arnicine, glucose, malic acid, saponin.
Symptoms: can cause gastroenteritis, quickening of heartbeat, trembling, cold sweat and, in extreme cases, death by asphyxia. Externally, blisters and erysipelous eruptions.
Treatment: professional.

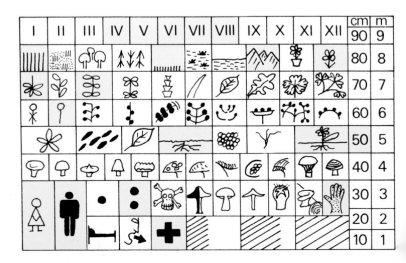

Cuckoo-pint, Lords and ladies

Araceae

Description: tuberous perennial; leaves glossy, sometimes spotted, on long stalks; flowers green, erect spathe with purple or yellow central spike (spadix); berries red in clusters.
Active principles: aroine, saponin, cyanogenetic glycoside, oxalates.
Symptoms: acute gastroenteritis, vomiting, weakness and collapse; death rare. Juices can cause dermatitis.
Treatment: symptomatic first aid; professional in severe cases.

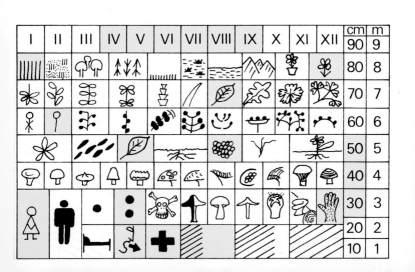

62 *Arum maculatum* L.

Cuckoo-pint, Lords and ladies
Fruiting heads

Araceae

Italian arum
Araceae

Description: tuberous perennial; yellow spadix, one-third as long as the spathe, the latter usually whitish; leaves first appearing in autumn, white-veined; longer winter leaves green-veined; berries red in clusters.

Active principles, Symptoms and Treatment: as for *A. maculatum*.

I	II	III	IV	V	VI	VII	VIII	IX	X	XI	XII	cm	m
												90	9
												80	8
												70	7
												60	6
												50	5
												40	4
												30	3
												20	2
												10	1

Deadly nightshade

Solanaceae

Description: herbaceous perennial, branched; leaves large, entire with axillary buds; flowers tubular, purplish, up to 5cm long, borne singly along stems; fruits: purple-black berries. Prefers waste places, ruins, roadsides.
Active principles: alkaloids (josciamine, atropine, belladonnin).
Symptoms: dilation of pupils, rapid heartbeat, cerebral excitement, trembling; followed by prostration, coma and death from asphyxia.
Treatment: professional.

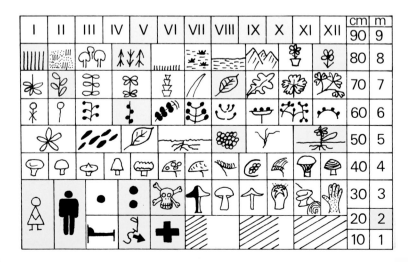

White bryony, Devil's turnip
Cucurbitaceae

Description: perennial climber, tuberous roots (can be mistaken for turnips or parsnips); long stems with tendrils; leaves palmate; flowers small, greenish in clusters of up to 5; berries red or orange with several yellow-black seeds.
Active principles: glycosidic substances (bryonin, bryonidin).
Symptoms: vomiting, abdominal pain, diarrhoea. Juice can cause irritation of skin.
Treatment: professional.

I	II	III	IV	V	VI	VII	VIII	IX	X	XI	XII	cm	m
												90	9
												80	8
												70	7
												60	6
												50	5
												40	4
												30	3
												20	2
												10	1

Marsh marigold   Ranunculaceae

Description: perennial, forming tufts; thick, creeping roots; leaves glossy on long stalks, usually springing from rootstock; flowers yellow.
Active principles: protoanemonin (leaves), unstable to drying; tannin, saponin.
Symptoms: sap can cause dermatitis; if ingested, mouth inflammation and gastroenteritis.
Treatment: symptomatic.

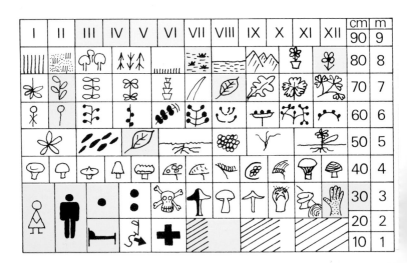

Hemp, Marihuana
Cannabinaceae

Description: annual herb, leaves with 5 to 7 dentate leaflets; flowers small, green; fruits: achenes. Characteristics differ in various cultivars; generally cultivated for fibre and oil, and widely naturalised.
Active principles: tetrahydro-cannabinols (inhaled from dried plant material and resin).
Symptoms: individually variable; generally euphoria and elation followed by heightened sensitivity and hallucinations, depression and comatose sleep. Death occurs in overdoses.
Treatment: professional.

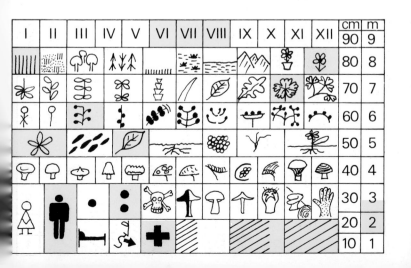

I	II	III	IV	V	VI	VII	VIII	IX	X	XI	XII	cm	m
												90	9
												80	8
												70	7
												60	6
												50	5
												40	4
												30	3
												20	2
												10	1

Greater celandine, Swallow-wort Papaveraceae

Description: perennial; branched, brittle stem; thick orange sap; leaves deeply lobed; flowers small, yellow, terminal; fruits: elongated capsules with several black seeds.
Active principles: alkaloids (chelidonine, cheleritrine, protopine).
Symptoms: external: severe skin irritation; internal: gastroenteritis with diarrhoea; can be fatal.
Treatment: symptomatic and/or professional.

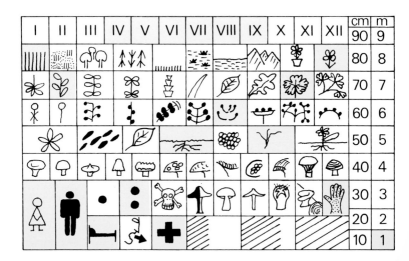

Traveller's joy, Old man's beard   Ranunculaceae

Description: perennial climber (up to 30m), twisting leaf stalks; leaves pinnate; flowers greenish white; fruits: long feathery tails on ripe carpels.
Active principles: similar to protoanemonin.
Symptoms: external: skin sores; internal: violent diarrhoea, enteritis; can be fatal.
Treatment: professional.

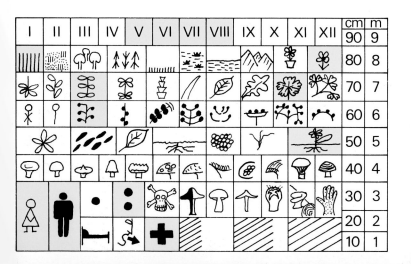

Hemlock, Poison hemlock   Umbelliferae

Description: biennial; fleshy white root, spindle-shaped; ridged hollow stems usually with purple spots; basal leaves large on long stems, upper ones sessile, all glossy green, darker on the upperside, compoundly pinnate with serrated margins; flowers white, small; fruits compressed, with wavy ridges.

Active principles: alkaloids (unstable) including coniine, conidrine and coniceine.

Symptoms: trembling, muscular incoordination and paralysis, occasionally convulsions, weak heartbeat, coma and respiratory failure leading to death.

Treatment: professional.

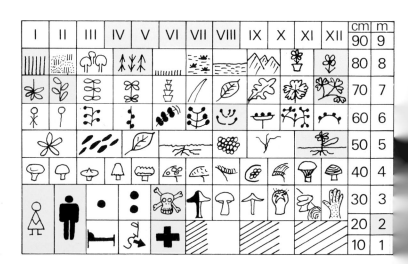

Spurge laurel, Wood laurel

Thymelaeaceae

Description: evergreen shrub; thick stems; leaves glossy and tough, in clusters on tip of branches; flowers yellowish, from leaf axils in spring; fruits: dark blue berries.
Active principles: coumarin glycosides.
Symptoms and Treatment: as *D. mezereum* (No 3).

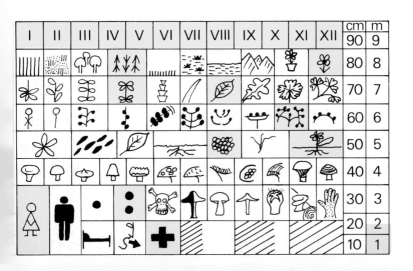

Thorn apple, Jimson weed

Solanaceae

Description: branched annual; leaves elliptic, variable in size; flowers white or violet in fork of branches, in summer; fruits: prickly capsules with several black seeds. Weed of cultivated areas.
Active principles: stable alkaloids (atropine, scopolamine, hyoscyamine).
Symptoms: unquenchable thirst, vomiting, enlarged pupils, delirium, jumbled speech, nervous twitches and convulsions; death follows in overdoses. Some symptoms may continue for several days.
Treatment: professional.

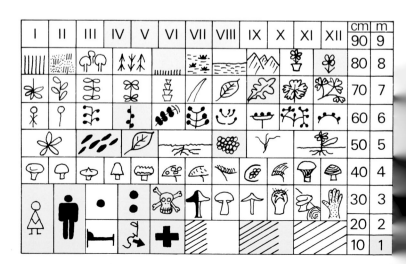

Spindle tree   Celastraceae

Description: deciduous shrubby tree; leaves with serrated margins; 4 angled twigs; flowers greenish in groups; fruits: 4 lobed, dark pink, orange arils with seeds.
Active principles: glycosides (evobioside, evomonoside, evonoside) plus bitter substance.
Symptoms: vomiting, diarrhoea, unconsciousness (can take several hours to show).
Treatment: symptomatic/professional.

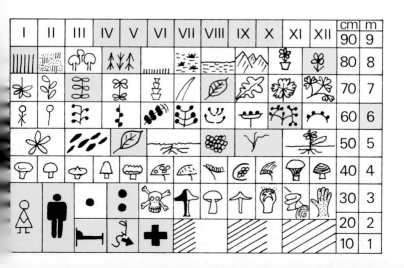

Caper spurge
Euphorbiaceae

Description: herbaceous biennial; leaves bluish green; flowers small; fruits lobed, with single seed.
Active principles: euphorbin (in sap and fruits).
Symptoms: drastic purgation, gastroenteritis; skin irritation and blisters.
Treatment: symptomatic.

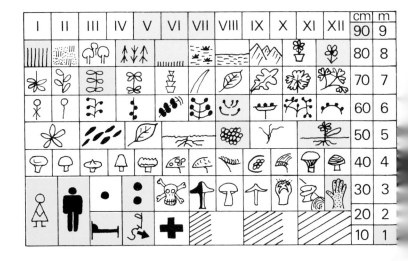

Sun spurge, Wartwort   Euphorbiaceae

Description: annual herbaceous; leaves spirally arranged, then in whorls, longer at top of stem; flowers unisexual, yellowish; fruits 3 lobed with 3 seeds.
Active principles: euphorbin.
Symptoms and Treatment: as *E. lathyris*.

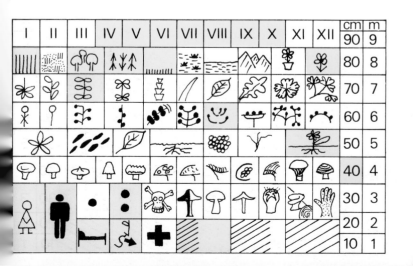

Petty spurge
Euphorbiaceae

Description: erect
annual; short stems
branching from base;
leaves pale green; flowers
with half-moon shaped
involucral glands with
slender horns; fruits with 3
seeds.
**Active principles,
Symptoms and
Treatment:** as for *E.
lathyris*. Reported to have
caused death in man.

I	II	III	IV	V	VI	VII	VIII	IX	X	XI	XII	cm	m
												90	9
												80	8
												70	7
												60	6
												50	5
												40	4
												30	3
												20	2
												10	1

Beech
Fagaceae

Description: deciduous tree up to 30m; smooth trunk and branches; leaves entire, veined; axillary female flowers, male flowers in catkins; seeds sharp-angled in 4 valved, woody, spiny cup.
Active principles: saponin glycoside or thiaminase.
Symptoms: severe abdominal pain, nausea, diarrhoea; in extreme cases convulsions and death.
Treatment: symptomatic/professional.

I	II	III	IV	V	VI	VII	VIII	IX	X	XI	XII	cm	m
												90	9
												80	8
												70	7
												60	6
												50	5
												40	4
												30	3
												20	2
												10	1

Alder buckthorn, Black alder
Rhamnaceae
Syn. *Rhamnus frangula* L.

Description: deciduous shrub; branches erect, alternate; leaves entire; axillary flowers whitish green, small, in spring; berries red then black.

Active principles: bark: rhamnotoxin (irritant and emetic), glycofrangulin (laxative); toxic glycosides.

Symptoms: vomiting, abdominal pain, violent diarrhoea; poisoning rare.

Treatment: symptomatic.

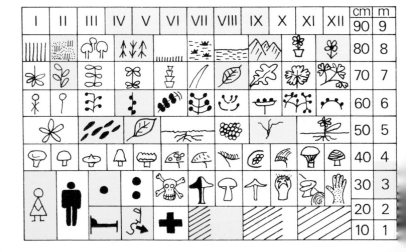

Great yellow gentian
Gentianaceae

Description: erect perennial; leaves large, rounded, veined; flowers in axillary and terminal whorls, golden yellow; fruits, ovoid; seeds, brown.
Active principles: gentiamarin, gentiine, gentiopicrin.
Symptoms: gastrointestinal.
Treatment: symptomatic.

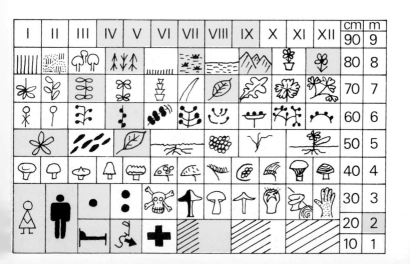

Henbane

Solanaceae

Description: annual/biennial; erect, branching, hairy; flowers bell-shaped, yellow/white, purple-veined, in leaf axils; fruit: globular capsule. Dryish habitats.
Active principles: alkaloids (hyoscyamine, scopolamine, atropine).
Symptoms: delirium, excessive salivation, impaired vision, rapid heartbeat, convulsions, coma; death possible.
Treatment: professional.

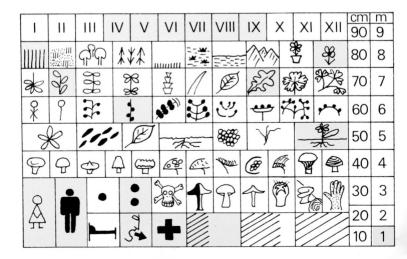

Common St John's wort

Hypericaceae

Description: perennial, rhizomatous rootstock; erect stem with 2 ridges; leaves with glandular dots; flowers yellow (July–Sept); fruits: capsules.
Active principles: hypericin (photodynamic pigment).
Symptoms: photosensitisation, mainly in livestock (redness and itching of skin, sores). Poisoning of humans not recorded, but guard against the leaves and flowers.

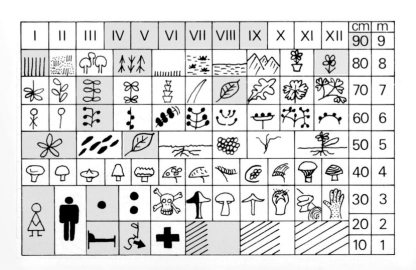

82 *Ilex aquifolium* L.

Holly   Aquifoliaceae

Description: evergreen shrub up to 12m; leaves toothed, glossy, spiny; flowers small, white (Apr–June); fruits red, globular (winter).
Active principles: a glycoside and an alkaloid (theobromine).
Symptoms: vomiting and purging; can kill children.
Treatment: emetics, then professional.

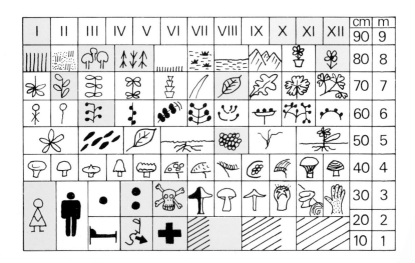

May lily   Liliaceae

Description: perennial rhizomatous; stems erect; flowers white; fruits: red globular berries.
Active principles: glycosides similar to digitalin.
Symptoms: not recorded.
Treatment: report to a doctor all cases of ingestion.

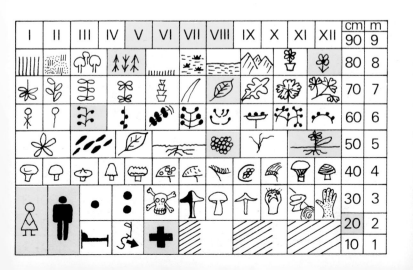

Mandrake

Solanaceae

Description: perennial, thick taproot; leaves basal, blunt, growing larger in autumn; flowers bell-shaped on short stalks; fruits: yellow-orange berries.
Active principles: hyoscyamine, mandragorin.
Symptoms: insensitivity, sedation, often heavy and leading to coma and death.
Treatment: professional.

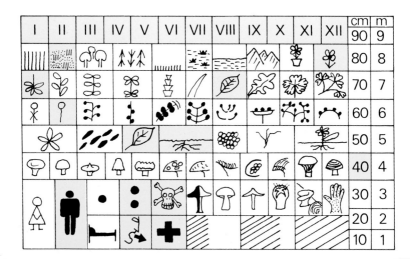

Dog's mercury, Herb mercury   Euphorbiaceae

Description: perennial on creeping rootstock; erect hairy stem; leaves toothed; flowers tiny, greenish; fruits hairy, 2-lobed with 2 seeds.
Active principles: volatile oil (destroyed by drying or boiling).
Symptoms: severe gastroenteritis.
Treatment: symptomatic.

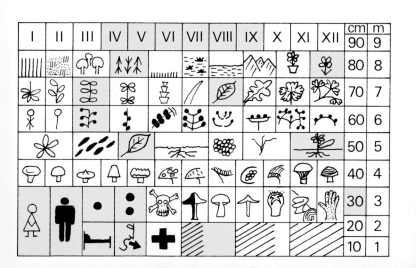

Bitter gourd, Balsam pear

Cucurbitaceae

Description: annual climber; flowers yellow, tubular; fruits ovoid, pointed and warty, green ripening to orange; pulp red; seeds grey-brown.
Active principles: purgatives (cucurbitacins).
Symptoms: vomiting, diarrhoea.
Treatment: symptomatic.

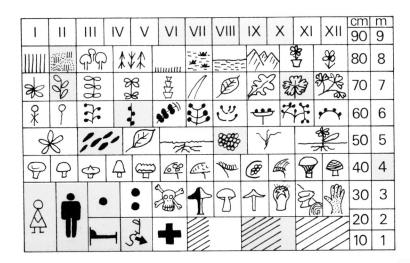

Water dropwort

Umbelliferae

Description: perennial; roots yellowish, thick and tuberous, in a clump; branched hollow stem; leaves compound, deeply divided; flowers white, tiny, in compound globular umbels; the juice turns yellow in the air. Seeds cylindrical.
Active principles: oenanthetoxin.
Symptoms: convulsions, excessive salivation, dilation of pupils, followed by death (rapid, sometimes without symptoms).
Treatment: professional.

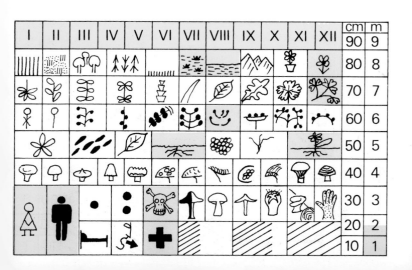

Star of Bethlehem

Liliaceae

Description: bulbous perennial; basal leaves; flowers on leafless stalks; leaves grooved above, with white band.
Active principles: alkaloids.
Symptoms: nausea, general gastrointestinal disturbances.
Treatment: symptomatic.

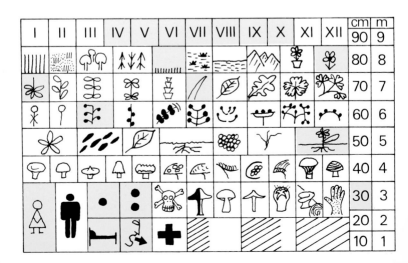

Corn poppy

Papaveraceae

Description: annual; hairy stems and leaves; scarlet flowers; fruit: smooth, round capsule; several black seeds.
Active principles: alkaloids (rhoedine).
Symptoms: gastrointestinal with drowsiness.
Treatment: symptomatic.

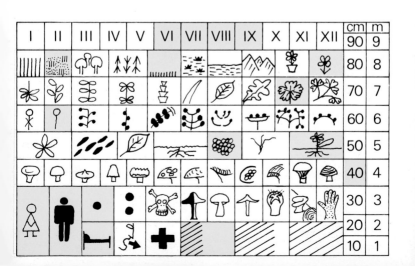

Herb Paris

Liliaceae

Description: herbaceous perennial; leaves terminal rosettes; flowers greenish yellow; blue-black berry with several seeds (children can mistake them for bilberries).
Active principles: paridine, paristyphinine.
Symptoms: nausea, diarrhoea, abdominal pain, headache, respiratory failure.
Treatment: symptomatic/professional.

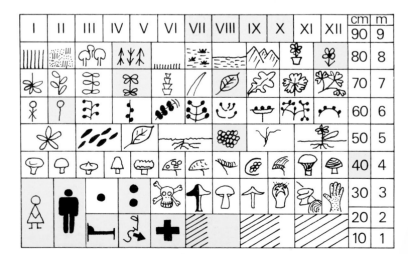

American mistletoe   Loranthaceae

Description: parasite of deciduous trees; bushy growth; flowers small, axillary; berries globular, whitish.
Active principles: tyramine, betaphenylethylamine.
Symptoms: gastroenteritis; possible failure of cardiovascular system.
Treatment: professional.

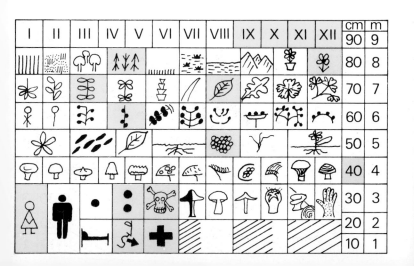

Pokeweed, Pigeon berry

Phytolaccaceae

Description: perennial taproot; tall stem; leaves petiolate; flowers small, greenish; shiny purple berries. Common in USA.
Active principles: unidentified.
Symptoms: stomach burn, vomiting, diarrhoea, sweating, disturbed vision, respiratory troubles. Can be fatal.
Treatment: professional.

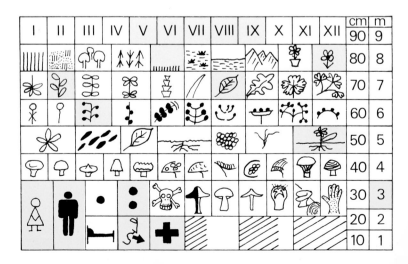

May apple
Berberidaceae

Description: perennial rootstock; large irregular leaves; flowers white, single; berry yellow, fleshy, many-seeded.
Active principles: podophyllin and other toxic substances.
Symptoms: gastrointestinal; purging, vomiting. Working with the powdered root can also cause conjunctivitis and keratitis.
Treatment: professional.

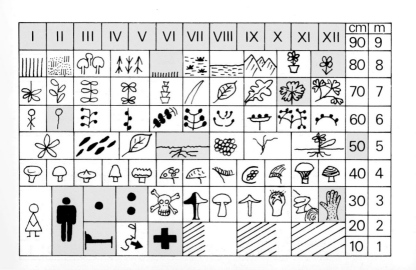

Common
buttercup,
Meadow
buttercup
Ranunculaceae

Description: perennial;
stem erect, hairy; leaves
stalked, hairy, segmented;
flowers shiny yellow;
achenes.
Active principles:
protoanemonin,
ranunculin.
Symptoms: external:
vesication; internal: severe
gastroenteritis.
Treatment:
symptomatic.

I	II	III	IV	V	VI	VII	VIII	IX	X	XI	XII	cm	m
												90	9
												80	8
												70	7
												60	6
												50	5
												40	4
												30	3
												20	2
												10	1

Celery-leaved buttercup   Ranunculaceae

Description: annual; stem erect, branched; leaves dark, serrated; flowers small yellow; achenes.
Active principles: as *R. acris*.
Treatment: professional.

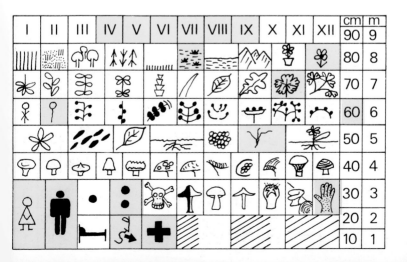

Common buckthorn

Rhamnaceae

Description: shrub, branched and spiny; axillary flowers; berries green to black, contain up to 4 seeds.
Active principles: rhamnoemodine, rhamnocathardin, shesterin (glycosides), saponin.
Symptoms: severe thirst, vomiting, violent diarrhoea.
Treatment: symptomatic; professional in severe cases.

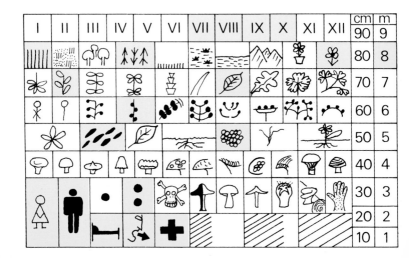

Alpenrose

Ericaceae

Description: woody evergreen shrub; glossy leaves; red flowers; oblong seed capsules.
Active principles: arbutin, aricolin, rhodoxantin.
Symptoms: vomiting, vertigo, delirium.
Treatment: professional.

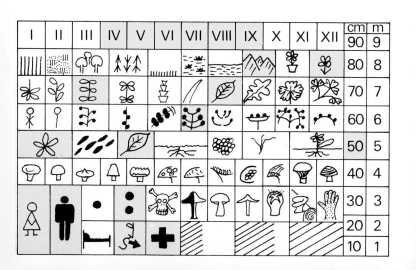

Rue   Rutaceae

Description: perennial; erect stem, branched; leaves fleshy, spotted with glands; flowers terminal, yellowish; fruits: globular capsules with black, kidney-shaped seeds.
Active principles: furocoumarins, tannins, xantotoxins.
Symptoms: diarrhoea, internal haemorrhage (can cause abortion); photosensitivity.
Treatment: professional.

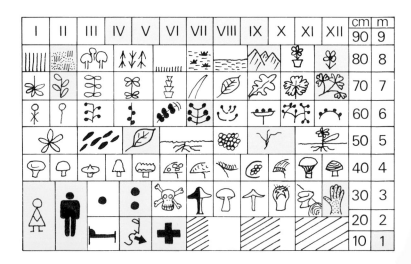

Elder
Caprifoliaceae

Description: shrubby
bush to small tree;
deciduous; composite
leaves with lanceolate
leaflets; flowers creamy;
berries black, globular,
containing several seeds.
Active principles:
sambucine, sambunigrin
(bark), sambucigrin.
Symptoms: violent
purgation; nausea from
raw (or unfermented)
berries; fresh leaves and
berries can irritate the
skin.
Treatment:
symptomatic.

Soapwort, Hedge pink

Caryophyllaceae

Description: perennial; ribbed leaves; flowers pink, often double; fruits: toothed capsules.
Active principles: saponin glycosides.
Symptoms: gastrointestinal; depression of the nervous system.
Treatment: symptomatic.

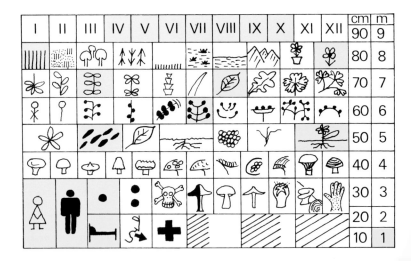

Ragwort, Benweed

Compositae

Description: injurious perennial weed; stem erect, branched; leaves deeply dissected; flowers yellow, surrounded by bracts; achenes.
Active principles: pyrrolizidine alkaloids.
Symptoms: toxic cyrrhosis of the liver in the long term; often none in the short term, or constipation, loss of condition, signs of jaundice.
Treatment: symptomatic/professional.

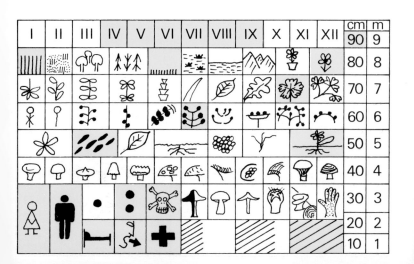

Woody nightshade

Solanaceae

Description: climbing or trailing woody perennial; flowers borne opposite the leaves, deep purple-blue; fruits: red drooping berries.
Active principles: alkaloids (solacein, dulcamarin).
Symptoms: gastric pain, constipation or diarrhoea; weakness, drowsiness and paralysis after larger amounts (over 6 berries).
Treatment: symptomatic/professional.

I	II	III	IV	V	VI	VII	VIII	IX	X	XI	XII	cm	m
												90	9
												80	8
												70	7
												60	6
												50	5
												40	4
												30	3
												20	2
												10	1

Black nightshade

Solanaceae

Description: annual/biennial, erect herbaceous; leaves petiolated; flowers white, small; berries green to black, attractive to children.
Active principles: glyco-alkaloids.
Symptoms and Treatment: as *S. dulcamara*.

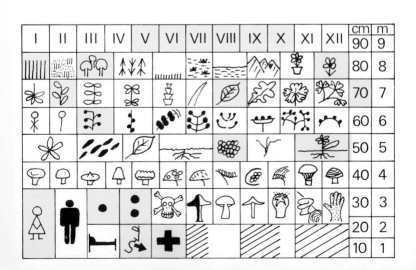

Black bryony

Dioscoreaceae

Description: blackish fleshy root; twining unbranched stems; leaves cordate, stemmed; flowers greenish yellow; berries oval, red when ripe.
Active principles: little known but similar to bryonin.
Symptoms: burning and blistering of the mouth, abdominal pain, diarrhoea; can be fatal.
Treatment: give plenty of milk, then professional.

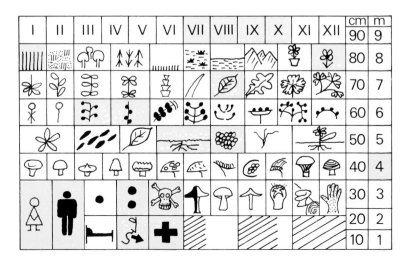

Yew   Taxaceae

Description: evergreen tree, sometimes up to 10m; leaves narrow, dark, in 2 opposite rows; flowers small, yellowish; berries bright red, with 1 seed.
Active principles: alkaloids (taxine, ephedrine), volatile oils.
Symptoms: vomiting, abdominal pain, diarrhoea, convulsions, delirium, cardiovascular paralysis; death very sudden and survival not common.
Treatment: professional.

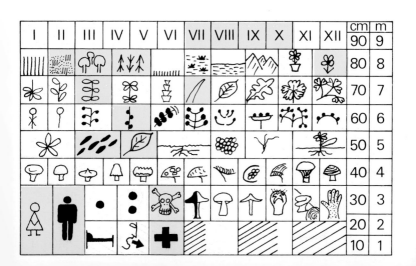

Poison ivy
Anacardiaceae
Syn. *Rhus*
toxicodendron L.

Description: woody vine,
variable; leaves trifoliate;
flowers small, whitish;
berries brownish yellow
with waxy, white flesh
striped black. Common in
USA.
Active principles:
urushiol (resin).
Symptoms: dermatitis
with blisters and vesicles.
Treatment:
symptomatic.

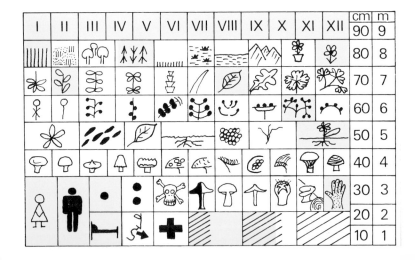

False hellebore
Liliaceae

Description: herbaceous tuberous plant; erect stem; basal leaves grooved and broad, upper leaves narrower; flowers whitish/yellowish/greenish; fruits: trilobed capsules with flat seeds.

Active principles: protoveratrine (alkaloid), veratramine, veratroin, vetralbine, jervine.

Symptoms: burning of mouth, tongue and throat; thirst, vomiting, diarrhoea, muscle cramps, slow pulse rate, breathing difficulties, collapse.

Treatment: emulcents/professional.

I	II	III	IV	V	VI	VII	VIII	IX	X	XI	XII	cm	m
												90	9
												80	8
												70	7
												60	6
												50	5
												40	4
												30	3
												20	2
												10	1

White hellebore   Liliaceae

Description: perennial rootstock; leafy stems; leaves in 3 rows, lower ones oval, upper ones lanceolate; flowers greenish; fruits: 3 celled capsule with several seeds.
Active principles: alkaloids.
Symptoms: depression of cardiovascular system; salivation, headaches, hallucinations, breathing difficulties, collapse.
Treatment: professional.

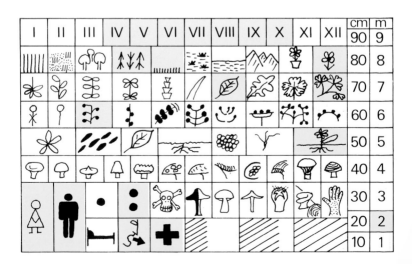

Mistletoe
Loranthaceae

Description: perennial parasite of deciduous trees; round branched stems; leaves evergreen, round; flowers yellowish; berries white, single seed.
Active principles: amines (acetylcholine, choline, viscotoxin).
Symptoms: gastrointestinal disturbances.
Treatment: symptomatic.

I	II	III	IV	V	VI	VII	VIII	IX	X	XI	XII	cm	m
												90	9
												80	8
												70	7
												60	6
												50	5
												40	4
												30	3
												20	2
												10	1

Fly agaric

Description: cap red, globular to plane, with white warts; white gills and stipe; flesh white; grows in tufts.
Active principles: mycoatropine, muscarine, ibotenic acid.
Symptoms: rapid; pain, diarrhoea, vomiting; excessive salivation and perspiration. Hallucinations, delirium, convulsions, coma and respiratory failure precede death. Mild cases recover in a few hours. Rarely fatal.
Treatment: symptomatic/professional.

I	II	III	IV	V	VI	VII	VIII	IX	X	XI	XII	cm	m
												90	9
												80	8
												70	7
												60	6
												50	5
												40	4
												30	3
												20	2
												10	1

Panther cap, False blusher

Description: cap from conical to flat, yellowish brownish/purplish; white scales; bulbous base, wide ring; flesh white.

Active principles: muscarine, mycoatropine, mycotoxin.

Symptoms: gastrointestinal irritation, vomiting, diarrhoea; confusion, hallucinations, delirium, convulsions, coma, death by respiratory failure. Process rapid.

Treatment: professional.

I	II	III	IV	V	VI	VII	VIII	IX	X	XI	XII	cm	m
												90	9
												80	8
												70	7
												60	6
												50	5
												40	4
												30	3
												20	2
												10	1

Death cap

Description: cap conical to flat, smooth, yellowish/greenish/brownish/blackish; gills white; flesh white; bulbous foot.
Active principles: phalloidin, phalloin, amanitine (alpha, beta and gamma).
Symptoms: slow: intermittent attacks of abdominal pain, diarrhoea, vomiting, intense thirst, weak pulse, cramps in legs; deep coma, cyanosis and jaundice (2–3 days); death within 5 to 10 days. Long-term damage to internal organs in case of survival.
Treatment: professional.

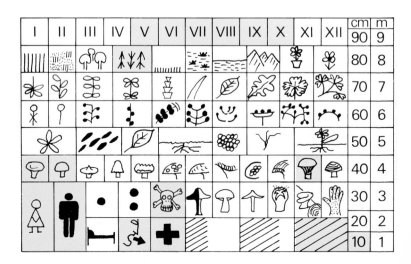

Fool's mushroom, Spring amanita

Description: cap white, top tinged pink/ochre; stipe white, slender, with ring, bruising to pink/ochre; gills white; flesh white; taste acid.
Active principles: similar to *A. phalloides*.
Symptoms and Treatment: as for *A. phalloides*.

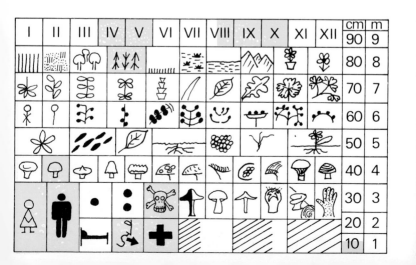

Destroying angel

Description: cap white, smooth, shiny; gills white; stipe white with woolly flakes; thin white ring; bulbous foot; flesh white; smell unpleasant.
Active principles: similar to *A. phalloides*.
Symptoms and Treatment: as for *A. phalloides*.

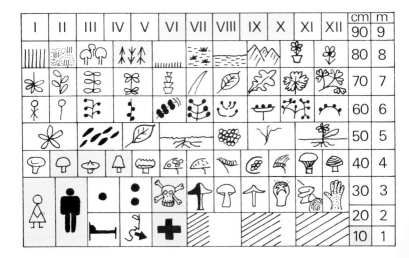

Red-stalked bolete

Description: cap reddish brown to greenish brown; tubes yellow turning bluish when touched; pores orange to red; stipe red-spotted; flesh yellow turning blue when broken, pink in the foot.
Active principles: unidentified.
Symptoms: gastrointestinal if eaten raw.
Treatment: symptomatic/professional.

Boletus luridus **Schaef. ex Fries**

Lurid bolete

Description: cap hemispherical to plane, ochraceous to brown, bruising to bluish; tubes yellow to greenish on red surface, turning blue in the air; pores orange to red; stipe yellow with red reticulation; flesh yellow in cap, red in stipe, bruising to blue.
Active principles: unidentified.
Symptoms and Treatment: as *B. erythropus* (115).

I	II	III	IV	V	VI	VII	VIII	IX	X	XI	XII	cm	m
												90	9
												80	8
												70	7
												60	6
												50	5
												40	4
												30	3
												20	2
												10	1

Description: cap with wavy margin and whitish down, turning blue to reddish when touched; tubes yellowish; pores irregular, yellow to red/orange, turning blue when touched; stipe yellow with red reticle, turns deep blue when touched; flesh yellow, deep blue in the air.
Active principles: unidentified.
Symptoms and Treatment: as previous boletes.

I	II	III	IV	V	VI	VII	VIII	IX	X	XI	XII	cm	m
												90	9
												80	8
												70	7
												60	6
												50	5
												40	4
												30	3
												20	2
												10	1

Devil's bolete

Description: cap velvety
to dry and cracked,
whitish to ash-grey; tubes
yellow to olive; pores
yellow to red and orange,
blue when touched; stipe
reddish, foot brown,
swollen, with reticulation
(red/brown/olive); flesh
spongy, whitish, turns to
blue in the air reverting to
white.
Active principles:
unidentified (muscarine?).
Symptoms: severe
gastroenteritis.
Treatment:
symptomatic/professional.

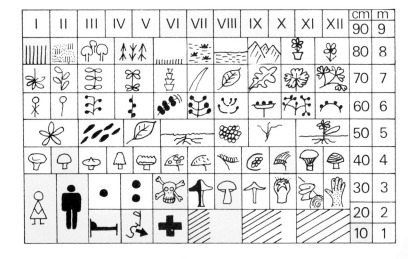

White-lead clitocybe

Description: cap white, smooth, occasionally spotted yellow and often with lobed margin; gills white to cream; stipe white, flaky to downy; flesh white; tastes and smells of flour.
Active principles: muscarine.
Symptoms: vomiting and diarrhoea, slow heartbeat, sweating, difficult breathing. Can be fatal.
Treatment: professional.

I	II	III	IV	V	VI	VII	VIII	IX	X	XI	XII	cm	m
												90	9
												80	8
												70	7
												60	6
												50	5
												40	4
												30	3
												20	2
												10	1

Clitocybe dealbata (Sow. ex Fries) **Kummer**

Description: cap buff, shiny; stipe whitish; flesh white; gills cream; smell faint.
Active principles: muscarine.
Symptoms: vomiting, diarrhoea, heavy secretions, slow heartbeat, impaired breathing. Can be fatal.
Treatment: professional.

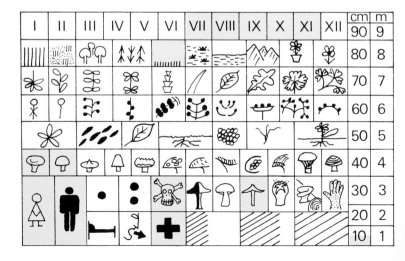

Clouded agaric

Description: cap smooth, shiny, whitish to brownish; gills creamy; stipe swollen at the foot, downy; flesh white; smell and taste acrid.
Active principles: unidentified.
Symptoms: can cause gastroenteritis when raw.
Treatment: symptomatic.

I	II	III	IV	V	VI	VII	VIII	IX	X	XI	XII	cm	m
												90	9
												80	8
												70	7
												60	6
												50	5
												40	4
												30	3
												20	2
												10	1

122 *Coprinus atramentarius* **Bull. ex Fries**

Common inkcap

Description: cap smooth/fibrillose/scaly, ochre to sooty; gills whitish to brown/black; stipe shiny white; flesh whitish to blackish; smell and taste good.
Active principles: unidentified.
Symptoms: if eaten with alcohol, reddening of face and body, increase in pulse rate, high temperature, weakness.
Treatment: symptomatic; do not drink alcohol, tea or coffee for a few days.

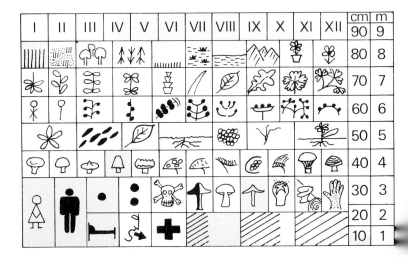

Description: cap with tiny reddish scales on whitish ground; stipe whitish with reddish scales on lower half, bruising reddish brown; flesh white in cap, yellowish in stipe, becoming deep yellow to red-brown; gills cream.
Active principles: unidentified.
Symptoms: gastroenteritis.
Treatment: symptomatic/professional.

I	II	III	IV	V	VI	VII	VIII	IX	X	XI	XII	cm	m
												90	9
												80	8
												70	7
												60	6
												50	5
												40	4
												30	3
												20	2
												10	1

Description: cap occasionally wavy, brown to red/orange; gills thick and rusty; stipe fibrillose, lighter than cap; flesh yellowish. Rare.
Active principles: unidentified.
Symptoms: gastrointestinal, severe to fatal.
Treatment: professional.

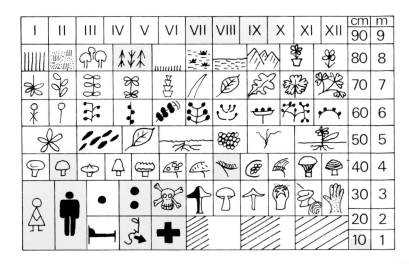

Livid agaric

Syn. *Rhodophyllus sinuatus, R. lividus, Entoloma lividum*

Description: cap ivory to grey; stipe white; flesh white; gills ochraceous becoming pink.
Active principles: unidentified.
Symptoms: violent nausea, diarrhoea, weakness; severe to fatal.
Treatment: professional.

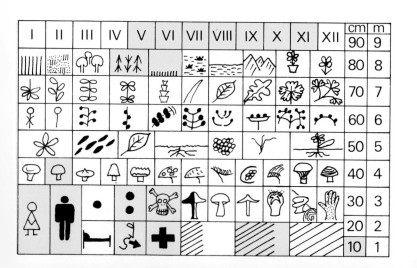

False morel

Description: cap folded, hollow, reddish brown; stipe pale, chambered; flesh whitish, brittle.
Active principles: helvellic acid, destroyed by heat; others unidentified.
Symptoms: severe to deadly: abdominal pain, vomiting, diarrhoea, cramps, giddiness, coma. Severe poisoning leads to liver and kidney damage.
Treatment: professional.

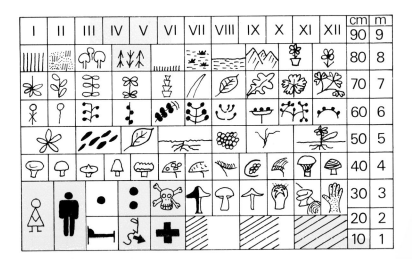

Poison pie

Description: cap yellowish or pink-brownish; gills white to ochre with rusty spots after wet weather; stipe same colour as cap, scaly at top; flesh whitish; smell and taste bitter, radish-like.
Active principles: unidentified.
Symptoms: nausea, indigestion, vomiting.
Treatment: symptomatic.

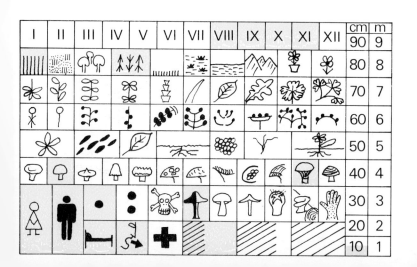

Brick cap

Description: cap orange, reddish at summit; gills grey to yellowish or greenish; stipe often curved, same colour as cap, with ring; flesh yellowish.
Active principles: unidentified.
Symptoms: can cause severe digestive troubles.
Treatment: symptomatic.

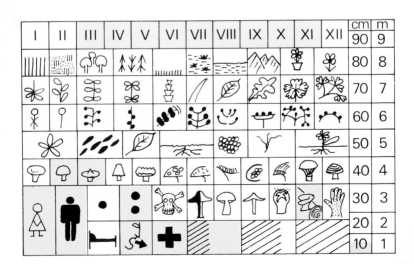

Description: cap shiny, sometimes cracked, ashy to yellow; gills yellowish; stipe white, fibrillose; flesh white; smell and taste earthy.
Active principles: muscarine.
Symptoms: vomiting, diarrhoea, slowing of heartbeat, difficult breathing, faintness. Can be serious.
Treatment: symptomatic/professional.

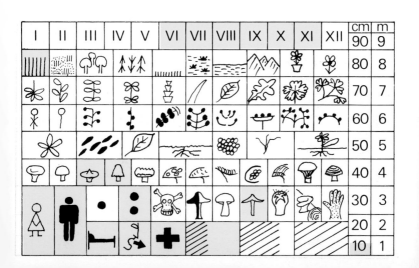

Earthy inocybe

Description: cap smooth, silky; gills grey to brown; stipe slender, fibrillose, same colour as cap; flesh white; taste and smell earthy.
Active principles: muscarine.
Symptoms and Treatment: as for *I. fastigiata*.

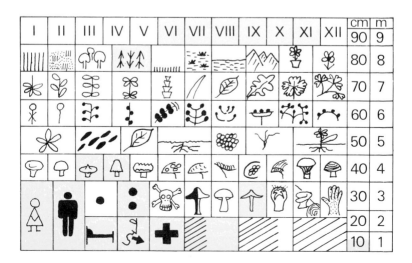

Description: cap with long, brown fibres and dense white down persisting on the umbo, often split or cracked; stipe white to brown; flesh white; gills greyish to buff.
Active principles: muscarine.
Symptoms: gastrointestinal.
Treatment: symptomatic/professional.

I	II	III	IV	V	VI	VII	VIII	IX	X	XI	XII	cm	m
												90	9
												80	8
												70	7
												60	6
												50	5
												40	4
												30	3
												20	2
												10	1

Description: cap brown with radial fibres; stipe whitish to concolour with cap; flesh whitish to buff; gills whitish to brown.
Active principles: muscarine.
Symptoms: gastrointestinal (see *I. geophylla*).
Treatment: symptomatic/professional.

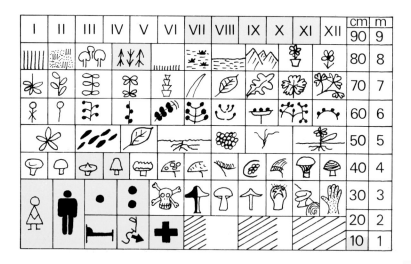

Red-staining inocybe

Description: cap whitish to yellowish to reddish, fibrillose, often cracked; gills white to rusty or brownish; stipe whitish spotted with red, staining red when bruised; flesh white; smell fruity.
Active principles: muscarine.
Symptoms: mainly as *I. fastigiata* but can be fatal.
Treatment: professional.

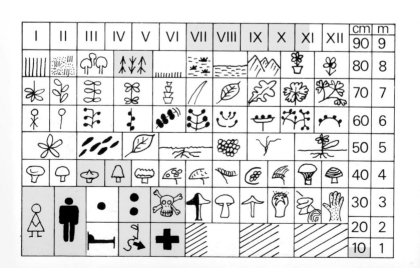

Woolly milkcap

Description: cap with involute margin, pinkish to orangy red, with concentrical areas; gills cream to pink; stipe same colour or paler than cap; flesh whitish, with milky juice.
Active principles: unidentified, destroyed by heat.
Symptoms: has caused violent gastroenteritis and even death.
Treatment: professional.

I	II	III	IV	V	VI	VII	VIII	IX	X	XI	XII	cm	m
												90	9
												80	8
												70	7
												60	6
												50	5
												40	4
												30	3
												20	2
												10	1

Poisonous lepiota

Description: cap pink to brown, scaly in rings; gills white; stipe concolorous with cap; flesh white, bruising to pink.
Active principles: unidentified.
Symptoms: gastrointestinal, disturbances of the nervous system. Could be deadly.
Treatment: professional.

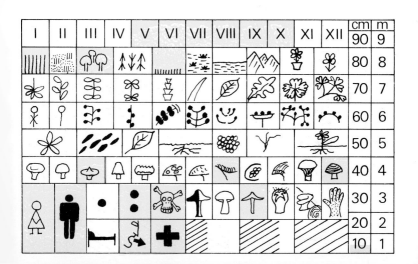

Syn. *N. staurospora*
Bres.; *Rhodophyllus
staurosporus* (Bres.) J.
Lange

Description: cap smooth,
nut-brown; gills greyish to
pink to rusty; stipe woolly,
concolorous with cap,
fibrous and furrowed;
flesh grey.
Active principles:
unidentified.
Symptoms:
gastrointestinal.
Treatment:
symptomatic.

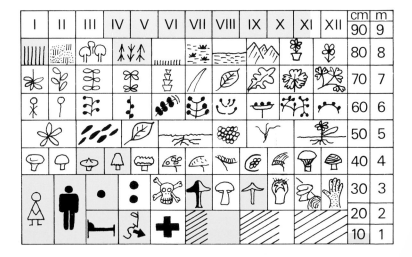

Syn. *Clitocybe olearia* (Fries ex DC.) Maire

Description: cap with involute to expanded margin, smooth and shiny, orange; gills yellow/orange, phosphorescent; stipe concolorous with cap; flesh yellowish. Grows in tufts with feet pressed together. Rare, except in Mediterranean areas.
Active principles: unidentified.
Symptoms: not recorded, probably gastrointestinal, severe.
Treatment: professional.

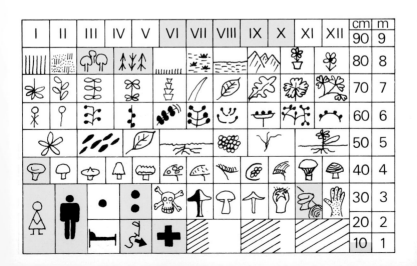

138 *Paxillus involutus* Batsch ex Fries

Inrolled paxil, Brown roll-rim

Description: cap ochraceous to brown, bruising to blackish; gills detachable, brownish, bruising purplish or dark brown; stipe fibrillose, tapering upwards; flesh ochre, blackish brown in the air.
Active principles: unidentified.
Symptoms: severe gastroenteritis (if raw or cooked when old), possibly deadly.
Treatment: symptomatic/professional.

I	II	III	IV	V	VI	VII	VIII	IX	X	XI	XII	cm	m
												90	9
												80	8
												70	7
												60	6
												50	5
												40	4
												30	3
												20	2
												10	1

Yellow stainer
Syn. *Agaricus xanthodermus* (Gen.)

Description: cap from globular to expanded, whitish/greyish, yellow when bruised, shiny; gills ash-white to pink to brown; stipe white bruising yellow; flesh white, yellow in the foot; smell and taste unpleasant.
Active principles: unidentified.
Symptoms: gastrointestinal cramps and severe upsets.
Treatment: symptomatic.

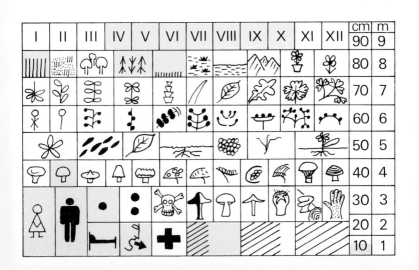

140 *Psilocybe semilanceata* (Fries ex Secr.)

Kummer

Description: cap with pinched umbo, yellowish brown, with olivaceous tinge; stipe white to creamy; flesh cream; gills pale to dark brown.
Active principles: psylocibin (hallucinogenic).
Symptoms: poisonous when raw (said to be fatal to children), harmless cooked.
Treatment: symptomatic/ professional.

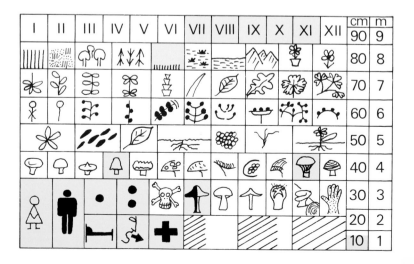

The sickener

Description: cap red or pink, discoloured by rain to whitish with pink spots; gills white or creamy; stipe wrinkled, white; flesh white.
Active principles: unidentified (muscarine?).
Symptoms: vomiting, diarrhoea, stomach pains and cramps.
Treatment: symptomatic.

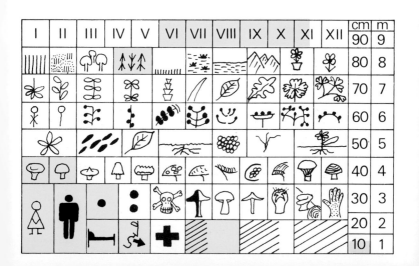

Common earthball
Syn. *S. citrinum* Pers., *S. vulgare* Horn.

Description: globular fruiting body, whitish to brownish, fleshy then corky; flesh pale when young, then purplish black and powdery.
Active principles: unidentified.
Symptoms: nausea, vomiting, giddiness, vision troubles, sweating, muscular spasms.
Treatment: symptomatic/professional.

I	II	III	IV	V	VI	VII	VIII	IX	X	XI	XII	cm	m
												90	9
												80	8
												70	7
												60	6
												50	5
												40	4
												30	3
												20	2
												10	1

Verdigris agaric

Description: cap bluish-green turning yellow when picked; gills ash to reddish grey; stipe concolorous with cap with whitish floccules; flesh whitish; smells and tastes of turnip.

Active principles: unidentified.

Symptoms: gastric upsets.

Treatment: symptomatic.

I	II	III	IV	V	VI	VII	VIII	IX	X	XI	XII	cm	m
												90	9
												80	8
												70	7
												60	6
												50	5
												40	4
												30	3
												20	2
												10	1

144 *Tricholoma tigrinum* **Schaeff. ex Fries**

Syn *T. pardinum* Quelet

Description: cap with inrolled to expanded margin; ash with brown tinge; gills white, tinged with yellow-green when old; stipe whitish; flesh whitish.
Active principles: unidentified.
Symptoms: gastrointestinal, severe.
Treatment: professional.

I	II	III	IV	V	VI	VII	VIII	IX	X	XI	XII	cm	m
												90	9
												80	8
												70	7
												60	6
												50	5
												40	4
												30	3
												20	2
												10	1

APPENDIX 1:
Notes to the plates

1 *Colchicum autumnale*   The bulbs can easily be mistaken for onions. All Liliaceae bulbs should be carefully kept out of the reach of children and pets.

2 *Convallaria majalis*   Both berries and flowers could be attractive to children. The plant is occasionally used in homeopathy (powdered roots) and perfumery.

3 *Daphne mezereum*   Children can mistake the berries for redcurrants. It is also dangerous to livestock.

5 *Delphinium ajacis*   Cultivated varieties are larger, with a wider range of colours. All *Delphinium* species and hybrids should be regarded as potentially dangerous.

7 *Digitalis purpurea*   Cultivated hybrids are grown in a wide range of colours. The leaves are the part used medicinally.

8 *Endymion* spp.   If you grow them in your garden, remember that children and pets can be tempted by stored bulbs. The familiar wild bluebell is one of the species in this genus (*E. nonscriptus*).

14 *Hedera helix*   Decoctions, tinctures and extracts of leaves are used in homeopathy as antineuralgics, antirheumatics and emmenagogues.

15 *Helleborus foetidus*   The plant was once used as a strong purgative or, externally, against lice. Either way, it proved lethal and was soon abandoned.

16 *Helleborus niger*   The green hellebore (*H. viridis*) is also poisonous. It grows wild on chalk and limestone; its radical leaves are divided into oblong, toothed segments; its flowers are drooping, yellowish green, two or three on stems about 10cm long.

17 *Hydrangea macrophylla*   The related *H. quercifolia* and *H. arborescens*, which grow wild in the USA and are cultivated elsewhere, are also dangerous. Another garden variety, *H. macrophylla* 'Lacecap' has heads of tiny flowers surrounded by usually white or pink bracts. It should be considered just as dangerous.

18 *Ipomoea purpurea*   The very similar species *I. tricolor* (Heavenly blue) is often grown in gardens and greenhouses; it contains hallucinogens normally used in the manufacture of 'purple hearts'. Symptoms and treatment are the same as for *I. purpurea*.

21 *Iris pseudacorus*   The rhizomes have been used for their emetic, diuretic, purgative and astringent properties; and the seeds, toasted, were once used as a coffee surrogate.

24 *Laburnum anagyroides*   This plant is also very dangerous to pets and livestock – it has killed horses. The related *Cytisus alpinus* is just as dangerous to both humans and animals.

26 *Lathyrus odoratus*   Horses seem particularly vulnerable to this plant.

L. sativus (Indian pea), *L. silvestris* (everlasting pea), *L. hirsutus* (hairy vetchling) and others are also dangerous.

29 *Mirabilis jalapa*   The roots are the source of a purgative drug used instead of jalap, which comes from *Ipomoea purga*.

30 *Narcissus pseudo-narcissus*   All thirty species in this genus should be considered poisonous, as well as the genera *Galanthus* (snowdrop), *Amaryllis*, *Crinum* and *Nerine*. Keep all stored bulbs out of reach of children.

31 *Nerium oleander*   The plant grows wild in the coastal areas of the Mediterranean. One single leaf can be fatal, or meat cooked while skewered onto oleander sticks.

34 *Papaver somniferum*   The subspecies *hortense*, with spotted petals, can still be found in gardens.

35 *Parthenocissus quinquefolia*   There are several forms in cultivation, all slightly different in leaf and vigour.

36 *Physalis alkekengi*   The berries are edible in salads and used in homeopathy.

40 *Prunus laurocerasus*   Children may be attracted by the berries, which are extremely poisonous when young, as are the kernels.

42 *Rhododendron ponticum*   Even the honey obtained from rhododendron flowers can be toxic. All rhododendron species should be regarded as equally dangerous.

44 *Robinia pseudoacacia.*   The flowers are used in perfumery and confectionery, and the leaves still have homeopathic applications.

47 *Solanum tuberosum*   Solanine is always present in potatoes, normally in quantities far too small to affect anyone. It tends to be concentrated in the layer next to the skin, so peel the tubers properly if they show any discoloration and always rub off any shoot which may be present. Normal boiling and baking seems to destroy most of the solanine.

53 *Aconitum napellus*   Also called Wolfsbane. Cultivated varieties have white, yellow, purple or rich blue flowers. About a hundred different species are known, plus several cultivated forms and hybrids.

55 *Actaea spicata*   *A. alba* and *A. racemosa* have also caused poisonings.

57 *Agrostemma githago*   Modern cultivation methods have almost eliminated the danger of wheat and other cereals being contaminated by this weed's seeds.

59 *Aquilegia vulgaris*   Columbine had its medicinal applications in the past, whether to treat wounds and skin diseases (leaf juice) or to cure afflictions of the liver and other internal organs (seeds). Cultivated varieties and hybrids are available in a wide choice of colours, some with bi-coloured blooms.

60 *Arnica montana*   This plant is used in homeopathy both externally (for bruises and sprains) and internally (febrifuge). It is also called mountain tobacco as it can be smoked instead of the real stuff.

61 *Arum maculatum*   Past medicinal uses included an infusion of leaves against coughs and stomach troubles. The roots were used as a source of starch, both in food and for stiffening clothes (eg the lace collars and cuffs of the Elizabethans).

64 *Atropa belladonna*   Guard against most Solanaceae, particularly the genera *Datura*, *Hyoscyamus* and *Solanum* (Nos 47, 72, 80, 102, 103).

65 *Bryonia dioica*   Past uses included a tincture for liver and spleen

ailments. It is still employed in homeopathy for its drastic and emetic properties.

66 *Caltha palustris*   The unopened buds can be used as capers. A colouring substance can be extracted from the plant and used to colour butter. Tinctures are used in homeopathy.

68 *Chelidonium majus*   Still used in homeopathy against ailments of the liver, respiratory ducts, digestive system, skin (warts).

70 *Conium maculatum*   The young plant can be mistaken for parsley, with fatal consequences unless it is well cooked. Children should avoid using the hollow stems as blow-pipes.

72 *Datura stramonium*   The leaves are used in homeopathy to treat asthma; tinctures and extracts are also still in use.

73 *Euonymus europaeus*   There are several cultivated species and varieties grown in gardens, some with variegated leaves.

75 *Euphorbia helioscopia*   Dangerous to livestock. In the past the juice was used to treat warts.

77 *Fagus silvatica*   The bark is widely used in homeopathic treatments as an expectorant, bechic, antiseptic and antipiretic. Edible oil can be extracted from the seeds; the fruits themselves can be toasted and used instead of coffee.

78 *Frangula alnus*   The bark is used to produce a homeopathic purgative.

79 *Gentiana lutea*   The root is used in homeopathy and liqueur manufacture. The aerial parts are a danger to livestock.

80 *Hyoscyamus niger*   Poisoning is rare but it has been known for the roots to be eaten in mistake for chicory or parsnips, and the seeds instead of beans. Its past uses in homeopathy include tinctures and extracts against toothache, rheumatism and arthrosis. Smoking the leaves is said to relieve asthma.

81 *Hypericum perforatum*   Regarded in homeopathy as a vulnerary, emollient, pectoral, vermifuge. It is used in the preparation of liqueurs.

86 *Momordica charantia.* It has naturalised on sandy soils in warm climates but is a native of Old World tropics.

87. *Oenanthe crocata*   The leaves have been mistaken for celery and the roots for parsnips. It is a most dangerous plant for livestock. Other species, such as *O. aquatica*, *O. fistulosa* and *O. silaifolia*, are equally poisonous.

89 *Papaver rhoeas*   The very young plants are sometimes eaten in salads and the petals are used to colour extracts and tinctures. The whole plant is considered to be bechic, sedative and emollient.

95 *Ranunculus sceleratus*   The most dangerous of buttercups, as the leaves are easily mistaken for parsley or celery.

97 *Rhododendron ferrugineum*   It is widely used in homeopathy for its diuretic, antirheumatic and antineuralgic properties.

98 *Ruta graveolens*   Rue has several homeopathic applications and is used as an aromatic in liqueurs.

99 *Sambucus nigra*   Widely used in traditional homeopathy, oenology and cookery, for its many properties and applications.

100 *Saponaria officinalis*   The leaves and stems were once soaked or boiled and the liquid used for washing. The plant is dangerous to livestock.

101 *Senecio jacobaea*   This is one of the most dangerous plants to livestock and should be eradicated, or prevented from spreading, by law. Poisoning of humans is not recorded in Europe.

102 *Solanum dulcamara*   Young branches and roots have been used in medicine as depuratives, diaphoretics and sedatives.

107 *Veratrum album*   *V. nigrum*, with dark purple flowers, is grown as an ornamental in gardens and is equally poisonous. *V. album* preparations are used as insecticides or external analgesics.

120 *Clitocybe nebularis, C. dealbata, C. rivulosa* and *C. morbifera* are very similar and equally dangerous.

126 *Gyromitra esculenta*   In some countries it is eaten after boiling and cooking and regarded as safe, but it has been known to cause cumulative poisoning in people who have eaten it for years without previous ill effects.

APPENDIX 2:
Other dangerous plants

Apocynum cannabinum (dogbane)   The leaves and tips contain the glycosides apocynein and cymarin, which can cause rising temperature and blood pressure, sweating, dilated pupils and gastrointestinal disturbances.

Arisaema triphyllum (syn. *A. atrorubens*, Jack-in-the-pulpit or Indian turnip)   Contains calcium oxalate crystals which cause burning and irritation of tissues.

Armillaria mellea (honey fungus)   Grows in tufts on tree trunks; can be eaten when very young and carefully cooked, but never when old or raw.

Artemisia absinthium (wormwood)   Flowers and leaves can cause allergic reactions.

Buxus sempervirens (box)   The leaves contain alkaloids and are said to be likely to cause dermatitis and, if ingested, enteritis (possibly fatal). Clippings have poisoned livestock.

Cestrum nocturnum (night-blooming jessamine)   Can cause alkaloid (atropine?) poisoning with hallucinations, tachycardia, nervous and muscular excitation, salivation and paralysis.

Cicuta maculata (water hemlock)   All parts contain cicutoxin. Symptoms after ingestion are swift – severe gastrointestinal pain in association with vomiting, salivation, mental frenzy and spasmodic convulsions with grinding of teeth alternating with quieter periods, dilated pupils and delirium. Death can occur within fifteen minutes. The pinnately compound leaves are not as deeply dissected as those of the *Conium maculatum* (No 70), the umbels are greenish and more flattened, and the stems, when cut, exude a toxic yellow oil.

Cicuta virosa (cowbane)   Very similar in apearance to, and just as poisonous as, *Cicuta maculata*. It is particularly toxic in early spring. The roots are sweet and have been mistaken for parsnips or potatoes; even a small piece can be fatal. It is often found in wet places.

Claviceps purpurea (ergot)   A long, curved, blackish fungus growing as a parasite on rye and other cereals. Although modern agricultural methods have rendered cases of human poisoning extremely infrequent in the Western World, they can still occur if infected flour is used in bread. Symptoms include drowsiness and vomiting, muscular contractions, hallucinations and gangrene – the latter due to the constriction of the finer capillaries which effectively stops the circulation, and causes tissues to die in areas farthest from the heart. Famous cases of ergotism have occurred in the past, particularly during the Middle Ages. Cattle can still be poisoned by infected hay.

Cryptostegia grandiflora (rubber vine).   The seeds are known to have caused death, preceded by severe gastrointestinal pain, vomiting and diarrhoea.

Cytisus alpinus A close relative of the laburnum (according to some authors, the same as *Laburnum alpinum*), it contains the same toxic substances and is equally dangerous.

Dicentra spp. (bleeding heart) The whole plant can cause allergies and is reported as possibly fatal if ingested.

Equisetum arvense (horsetail, mare's tail) Contains thiaminase and other toxic substances. Together with *E. palustre*, it is particularly dangerous to horses and cattle. When ingested, it causes loss of condition, unsteadiness and fast weak heartbeat.

Fagopyrum sagittatum (syn. *F. esculentum*, buckwheat). A well-known cause of photosensitivity in animals. The flour is occasionally used for human consumption and can give rise to allergic reactions in certain individuals.

Helvella gigas (syn. *Gyromitra gigas*) Contains toxic substances which are not always destroyed by cooking.

Juniperus spp. (junipers) Young leaves and shoots were once used in popular medicine, but are now considered dangerous. They can cause gastroenteritis and internal bleeding.

Lactuca virosa (syn. *L. silvestris*, wild lettuce) The sap contains bitter principles, several acids and other toxic substances. Although used in homeopathy (as a narcotic, sedative, analgesic, bechic), it can cause serious poisoning with nausea, fast heartbeat, headache, vertigo and cardiac paralysis.

Lepiota procera (parasol mushroom), *L. rhacodes* (shaggy parasol) and *L. excoriata* are all regarded as toxic when raw.

Lepista nuda (syn. *Rhodopaxillus nudus*) A poisonous mushroom when raw, it should be very carefully cooked before consumption.

Linum usitatissimum (flax) The seeds and the oil (linseed oil) can irritate the skin. Seeds and leaves contain a cyanogenetic glycoside which can cause excitement, irregular respiration, convulsions, paralysis and death. It affects animals fed on linseed cake.

Lobelia inflata (Indian tobacco) All parts contain several alkaloids and misuse of the plant can cause vomiting, weak heartbeat, weakness, fits of convulsions and coma. Deaths have been reported. This is the plant originally smoked by the American Indians. All species of *Lobelia*, including the cultivated ones, should be regarded as dangerous.

Lonicera spp. (honeysuckle) Best to keep well away from their berries!

Philadelphus spp. (mock orange) The fruits have been reported as extremely dangerous.

Philodendron spp. These common houseplants contain the highly irritant calcium oxalates.

Prunus serotina (wild black cherry) A tall tree with white/pink flowers followed by bunches of round black fruits with a single hard stone. The kernels contain a cyanogenetic glycoside and have killed children; the leaves are also toxic.

Pteridium aquilinum (bracken) All parts, particularly the rhizome, contain thiaminase and other toxic substances. Horses and cattle are particularly vulnerable.

Russula mairei (beechwood sickener) Common in deciduous woods, particularly beechwoods, in autumn, it is similar to *R. emetica* (No 141, which grows under pines) except for a much shorter stipe. *R. betularum*, a paler species growing under birches, is also poisonous.

Symplocarpus foetidus (skunk cabbage)   Calcium oxalate crystals make this plant extremely irritating to all mucous membranes.

Tanacetum vulgare (tansy)   Said to have caused dermatitis in susceptible individuals.

APPENDIX 3:
Treatment of plant-poisoning

As we have seen in Section II, poisons have always exercised a deep fascination on the human mind – a fascination which, in turn, generated the need to find antidotes, above all an antidote which would be effective against a wide range of poisons. For centuries, the powdered horn of the unicorn was regarded as such, but in the 1830s a Frenchman came up with the much more prosaic charcoal. M. Touery experimented on himself and, in front of the astonished eyes of the French Academy, swallowed ten times the lethal amount of strychnine immediately followed by half an ounce of charcoal – and walked away a healthy man.

In other parts of the world charcoal has a long history as antidote and general cure-all, but it is activated charcoal which has mostly been used in industrialised countries. Activation processes vary, but they all aim at creating an enormous amount of charcoal pores, the total surface of which can reach $90m^2$ ($c1,000$sq ft) per gram (.035oz). The huge absorption capacity of this surface renders activated charcoal an effective antidote against such poisons as antimony, arsenic, atropine, camphor, cocaine, digitalis, morphine, muscarine, nicotine, opium and stramonium. Until recently the antidote was effective only while the poisons were still in the stomach; since the 1960s, however, an instrument has been developed which uses activated charcoal to purify a patient's blood of many poisonous substances. Obviously, this is available only to hospitals; hence the need to seek professional help as soon as possible, in most cases of plant poisoning.

Activated charcoal is available from chemists in most Western countries, usually in the form of tablets and in conjunction with syrup of ipecac. Such antidote kits should prove very useful additions to the family medicine cupboard. However, in most cases activated charcoal is just not part of a household's supply of drugs, so let us see how best to cope with poisoning in run-of-the-mill circumstances.

You may be confronted with a child complaining of tummy pains. Has it eaten something? Is it still holding parts of a plant in its hand? Or can it lead you to a possible source of trouble? All this of course would help in assessing the cause of the complaint, as well as in deciding what to do next. If the child vomits (or is made to vomit, see below), parts of the plant like berries or leaves or seeds may be apparent in the vomit, which should in all cases be kept for medical examination.

Older people, suddenly scared of something they have eaten, should tell somebody else, possibly a doctor, or write it all down if nobody is around, and then seek help. Remember that a knowledge of what has happened prior to the appearance of the symptoms is vital to the identification of the latter, and consequently of their cause, and to the choice of appropriate treatment.

The symptoms themselves are extremely variable, as they depend on the individual and the circumstances of ingestion. Also, they may well be due to causes other than plant poisoning; in fact gastrointestinal upsets, such as vomit, diarrhoea and abdominal pain, are usually due to much more common causes. This is why a clear association with a toxic plant is needed, either in the form of plant residues in the vomit or as an admission or realisation of the plant having been eaten. Again, plant poisoning is only one of the possible causes of delirium, convulsions or excitation, coma or difficulty in breathing. A common symptom, however, is a very irregular or abnormal heartbeat (and pulse), while irritation and burning of the skin or mouth can be associated with the sap of certain plants – if you can rule out the bleach in the kitchen cupboard.

So what should you do? The first thing, if you suspect a poisonous plant has been ingested, is to make the person vomit, so that as little as possible of the toxic substance is absorbed into the system. Having made this point, I must also stress that vomit should never be induced if the victim is unconscious or if the toxic substance is highly irritant or even corrosive, as this would cause further damage. Vomiting can be induced by mechanical means (the familiar two fingers down somebody's throat) or by ingesting as large a quantity as possible of hot sweet milk or water with mustard. Milk, a good demulcent, should be given in all cases, either before and during the vomiting, or instead of it when vomiting is to be avoided. Eggs and vegetable oil can also be used, when irritating substances have been swallowed, but avoid administering salt in any form or for any reason.

If vomiting is induced, the patient should always be held with head below hips to prevent the vomit entering the lungs. Keep calm and try to keep the patient calm: excitation and panic increase the heartbeat thus speeding up the distribution of toxic substances, should they have already entered the blood flow.

Except in very few cases, when the substance and quantity ingested are clearly not dangerous, it is always advisable to seek medical help. This is particularly so if the patient's breathing is difficult or impaired, if he or she has lost consciousness, is shocked, suffering from convulsions or acute pains, turning blue or showing any other serious symptoms. Only hospitals can give gastric lavage and take all the necessary steps to combat the effects of the poison.

Very often even hospital treatment can deal only with the symptoms; in many cases the poison is unknown or, if known, no antidote exists. The only way to help the patient, then, is by administering appropriate drugs which counterbalance heart malfunction, respiratory problems, dehydration, hypothermia, convulsions, paralysis and other symptoms. This is termed symptomatic, or supportive, treatment; and only qualified staff with appropriate drugs and machinery can carry it out. In the captions to the plates, this is referred to as 'professional' treatment.

Apart from activated carbon, which can usually be used only with the help of highly sophisticated machinery, there are no really satisfactory antidotes available to doctors. Some cases of amanita poisoning can be treated by the injection, very early on, of an antiphalloidian serum, specially prepared and not readily available. Many of the drugs used in cases of plant poisoning are actually derived from other plants and are potentially poisonous themselves, their effect being the opposite of the symptoms they are used to alleviate.

To sum up, in order to help a person suspected of being poisoned, you can administer first aid geared at making the victim comfortable. You can relieve the symptoms ('symptomatic' in the captions) and can expell – by vomiting or neutralising with activated carbon tablets – as much as possible of the toxins. Beyond that, leave it to the experts.

BIBLIOGRAPHY

Altmann, H. *Poisonous Plants and Animals*, Chatto & Windus (1980)

Arnold, Harry L. *Poisonous Plants of Hawaii*, C. E. Tuttle (1968)

Chiej, R. *Piante Medicinali*, A. Mondadori (1982)

Dickinson, C. and Lucas, J. *The Colour Dictionary of Mushrooms*, Orbis Publishing (1979)

Emboden, W. *Narcotic Plants*, Studio Vista (1972)

Forsyth, A. A. *British Poisonous Plants*, Ministry of Agriculture, Fisheries and Food, HMSO No 161 (1980)

Gadd, Lawrence *Deadly Beautiful: The World's Most Poisonous Animals and Plants*, Macmillan (1980)

Hardin, James W. and Arena, James W. *Human Poisoning from Native and Cultivated Plants*, Duke (1973)

Kinghorn, A. Douglas, ed. *Toxic Plants*, Columbia University Press (1979)

Kingsbury, J. *Deadly Harvest*, G. Allen & Unwin (1967)

Limburg, Peter R. *Poisonous Plants*, Messner (1976)

Menscher, Walter C. *Poisonous Plants of the United States*, Macmillan (1975)

Nonis, U. *Mushrooms and Toadstools*, David & Charles (1982)

North, P. *Poisonous Plants and Fungi*, Blandford Press (1967)

Phillips, R. *Mushrooms*, Pan Books Ltd (1981)

Ricciuti, Edward R. *The Devil's Garden: Facts and Folklore of Poisonous Plants*, Walker & Co (1978)

Schmutzt, Ervin M. *Plants that Poison: An Illustrative Guide for the American Southwest*, Northland (1979)

Tampion, J. *Dangerous Plants*, David & Charles (1977)

Tichy, W. *Poisons – Antidotes and Anecdotes*, Sterling Publishing Co/Oak Tree Press (1977)

Viola, S. *Piante medicinali e velenose*, Istituto Geografico de Agostini (1968)

Wertheim, Alfred *Natural Poisons in Natural Foods*, Lyle Stuart (1974)

ACKNOWLEDGEMENTS

I am particularly grateful to the Italian mycologist, Umberto Nonis, for generously contributing his own photographs; and to Dr Christopher Grey-Wilson and Mr G. E. Cassidy for their help and support. Numbers refer to colour plates.

Photography:

U. Nonis: 113, 119, 124, 125, 135, 137, 144

C. Grey-Wilson: 4, 7, 10, 13, 25, 26, 34, 44, 45, 50, 52, 53, 57, 59,74, 79, 97, 99, 105, 107

G. E. Cassidy: 19, 20, 21, 22

A. W. Brand: 130, 143

H. Angel/Biofotos: 86, 90

L. Brown: 6

A. W. McDonald: 37

Oxford Scientific Films: G. A. Maclean, 70, 95, 100; Sean Morris, 43

Focal Point: Reg Davis, 17, 24, 27, 29, 36, 39, 41, 47, 56, 63, 66, 72, 76, 77, 78, 80, 84, 94, 98, 103, 115

Focus Picture Library: 9, 28, 40, 58, 69, 75, 81, 89

Harry Smith Horticultural Photographic Collection: 12, 23, 32, 33, 38, 46, 48, 49, 83, 92

Nature Photographers: F. V. Blackburn, 109, 126; D. Bronsall, 62; B. Burbidge, 31, 42, 60, 67, 87, 106, 108; A. A. Butcher, 134; B. Candy, 114; K. Carlson, 18; A. Cleave, 141; G. Dickson, 116, 117, 118, 120, 123, 129, 136, 139, 140; K. Handford, 35; J. V. and G. R. Harrison, 55; J. Hyett, 131, 132; E. A. Jones, 85, 128; D. Rae, 88, 93; P. Sterry, 111, 133

Slide Centre: 1, 2, 3, 5, 8, 11, 14, 15, 16, 30, 51, 54, 61, 64, 65, 68, 71, 73, 82, 96, 101, 102, 104, 110, 112, 121, 122, 127, 138, 142

INDEX

Figures in *italics* refer to colour plates